My Body, Their Baby

The true story of a woman who
offered to act as a surrogate for
her friend and discovered she had
to give up more than a baby.

By

Laurie Miller

The Reginald vanFenwick Press
Stoughton, MA

This is a true story based on the journals, notes and best recollections of Laurie Miller. In certain instances the names and identities of specific individuals and establishments have been changed to protect their privacy.

Front Cover: Artwork by Lisa C. Kaufman at Esprit d'art
email at espritdart@yahoo.com

Back Cover: Laurie Miller

Copyright © 2008 by Laurie Miller

Library of Congress Control Number: 2008935876
ISBN 13: 978-0-972-81696-0
ISBN 10: 0-972-81696-8

First Edition

Published by
The Reginald vanFenwick Press
Stoughton, MA

Manufactured in the United States of America

Dedication

There are people in our lives who possess infinite energy; a life force so fierce, so pervasive, that it can't help but leave a footprint. This energy cannot be stilled, even in death. Everyday I try to be half as good as you were. I hope I am making you proud.

Robert S. Kaufman

December 28, 1962- December 19, 1994

"As we look deeply within, we understand
our perfect balance.
There is no fear of the cycle of birth, life and death.
For when you stand in the present moment,
you are timeless."

Rodney Yee

Chapter Headings

Prologue

I hung up first, or did he? It was as if someone had called me from another dimension. I was cold, crying and shaking uncontrollably. Like a robot I walked into the kitchen, poured myself a large glass of red wine, and somehow made my way to the basement. I had to get the box. Like yesterday, I remembered putting it on the highest shelf in the closet, way in back, as if never intending to need it again. Through soggy eyes, I pulled it down. My knees gave way and I sat on the floor. I opened the box, and with hands trembling, began to dig through all the medical reports, bills, pictures, notes, magazines and more bills, until I found them. My journals.

"Mom?"

Startled, I looked up to see the worried eyes of my nine-year old daughter Sarah. "Are you okay?"

"No," I said bluntly. Maybe a better mother would have lied: *Everything is fine, honey, go back to what you were doing.* But our relationship has never been based on deception; she saw my tear-soaked face, and crouched beside me.

"What's going on? Who was that on the phone?"

I touched her face. "You were only two when it started," I sighed.

"When *what* started?"

"Something I should have told you about before now, but I wasn't sure you were ready to hear." I took a deep breath and wiped my tears. "I guess now's the time."

Baysville, Ontario, 1974

The skinny girl shivering on the dock at Camp New Moon looked around nervously. Her light brown hair, pulled back in a stubby ponytail, accentuated large brown eyes and an early summer tan. A bikini did nothing to conceal her bony figure.

At sixteen, I was a swim instructor for the first time, and approached her with a confidence I secretly didn't feel. "Ready for your test?"

"What do you mean?" she said. "I'm giving the test."

"How can you be giving the test if I'm giving the test?"

A smile took over her anxious features. "You must be Laurie!"

"Who are you?"

"I'm Meg. The other swim instructor."

"Oh! I mean, hi."

"Thought I was one of the campers, huh?"

"Well, I mean you're so... yeah. Sorry."

"It's okay. People always think I'm younger than I am. My mom says when I'm 30 I'll be glad."

We laughed. Thirty was like, a hundred years away.

"Where are you from?" I asked.

"Toronto. You?"

"New Jersey."

"I knew you were from the States, you have an accent. How come you're here?"

"My mom is friends with the owner."

The *bleeeet!* of a whistle reminded us that we were there to work. Together, we approached a group of chattering kids.

"Come on," Meg whispered, "I don't look *that* young,

do I?"

Yes! "No."

"Watch how bossy I can be." She clapped her hands and they all looked up. "Okay, everyone here for the testing?" As one, they nodded, wide-eyed; the way we did when we were campers. Meg and I swapped powerful grins. Oh, this was going to be a blast!

We spent the day deep water testing anyone who wanted boating equipment privileges. July in northern Ontario had done nothing to warm up the water, and as the campers jumped in, they gasped and struggled.

"Relax," I kept saying, "you'll be fine." A few feet up the dock I could hear Meg's voice: "Relax! Your body just needs to adjust to the temperature change. You'll be fine."

Like a pro, I tooted my whistle at a little boy who started to get out. "You haven't been treading water for five minutes, yet!" I pointed at my watch. "You have two minutes left."

"You're tough," Meg observed, checking off a camper and signaling another one to jump in.

"It's for their own good, they have to be prepared." I spotted a girl in a red bathing suit, and said sternly, "Hey, one more lap!"

"Glad *I* didn't have you," Meg teased.

Dinner was allegedly turkey and gravy. So gross. The option was peanut butter and jelly sandwiches. Also gross. To my surprise, Meg had both.

"Where do you put it?" I asked enviously. Even though I wouldn't want to be as skinny as her, I thought how fun it would be to just go ahead and eat whatever you wanted and never worry about gaining weight.

"Look." From her pocket she pulled out a plastic bag full of pills. *No way*, I thought; *a drug addict!* Speechless, I watched her take three... six... eight... and lost count. One after another, two or three at a time, washed down with a sip of what we called bug juice.

"What are you doing?" I finally asked.

"I have Cystic Fibrosis. Do you know what that is?"

I shook my head.

"My body makes too much mucous. I don't have the enzymes that break down food in my pancreas, and the mucous clogs up my lungs."

"How long have you had it?"

"I was born with it." She kept taking pills. "The green ones do the job of the enzymes. The others are vitamins and supplements. Can you believe how many I need?"

I shook my head again. "So you'll get better if you take them all?"

"No, there's no cure. I have to take them and exercise and eat a lot. My body works so hard fighting the CF that there's no energy left to make me gain weight."

"Wow! Is it hard to live like that, or are you used to it?"

"Used to it, sort of. Every morning I have to pound my chest to break up the mucous, and I have to do breathing treatments throughout the day. I take pills every single time I eat, whether it's a full meal or a piece of candy." At last the bag was empty. She folded it and put it back in her pocket. "This is the first time I've been away from home."

"Are you nervous?"

"A little."

"When I was a camper here my first year I had appendicitis and had to have emergency surgery. I was scared to death. I was sick for about a week before they figured out it was my appendix. They thought it was a stomach bug."

"Did your parents have to come get you?"

"No, my sister Lisa was here, and she called them every day. But being sick and so far from home was so hard."

"Well I don't think of myself as being sick. It's just the way I am, and I deal with it the way I have to. I think having emergency surgery would be way worse."

I didn't, because once my appendix was out I was all better. But of course I didn't say that. Off duty since 5:00, we watched the noisy campers get herded out by other counselors for evening activities, then Meg suggested we take a walk to the dock and watch the sun set over the lake.

"Is Lisa older or younger?" she asked on the way.

"Older. And I have a little brother, Rob."

"I have an older sister, too. We can't stand each other."

"How come?"

"Before I was born she was an only child for a pretty long time, and she liked it. I don't think she ever got over having to share my parents. She's pretty selfish."

"Maybe she's jealous because you got a lot of attention, being... " I didn't want to use the word *sick* again, so I amended swiftly, "having CF."

"Maybe. I don't know. I wish my parents had one more kid. I would love to have had a baby around, I love babies. Anyway, they got divorced when I was ten."

"I sometimes think my parents should get divorced," I said; my darkest and most shameful secret, and the first time I'd ever spoken it out loud. "All they do is fight."

Meg sighed in sympathy. We reached the dock and the setting sun was orange and romantic. "Did you see that really cute counselor-in-training? Neil?"

"Yes, but you know the rules. We're not allowed to get involved."

"I'm just saying he was cute. There was another one there who was cute too."

"Mark."

"Gorgeous blue eyes."

"We seriously have to stay away from them."

"We will." Her smile was mischievous. "You going to stay away from Greg, too?"

"Especially Greg. He's with Mandy. Ugh, she's such a bitch."

"She's a bitch to you because she can tell he likes you."

"What? He does not."

"Laurie, *please!* The way he was flirting with you at dinner?"

"Really?"

"Duh, Laurie!"

We laughed. I thought how lucky I was to have found such a great friend right away, and I know she was thinking it too, because she linked her arm in mine and said, "This is going to be the best summer *ever.*"

Part One

The Offer

"Let the record show that I hate this," I said.

"So noted," my husband Ken replied wearily as he straightened up with a groan. "Okay, all the dishes are packed. That leaves pots and pans, and then the kitchen is done."

"I mean, who in their right mind moves to Rhode Island?" I should have been helping, but felt justified in being grumpy and inflexible. Yes, I'd agreed to the five-year plan and that if things didn't work out with his new job we could move back to New Jersey. But that was last spring and it didn't feel real, I didn't think it would really happen. After all, he wasn't that excited about it either. His life insurance company was transferring all the reps to the home office, so it was go along or look for another job. And after 15 years with them, he felt invested.

"It's not a third world country, you know. It's actually part of the United States."

"Just such a big change. A new school for Mike. I have to quit my job, leave my family, and what about my brother?"

Ken's voice turned gentle. "Rob will be fine. People with AIDS are living much longer now, and he has a great doctor. We won't be that far away. You can visit anytime you want."

"I know, but..."

"Look on the bright side."

"There's a bright side?"

"You'll get to spend more time with the kids."

As if on cue, ten-month old Sarah wiggled into my lap. I nuzzled her neck, committed her baby fragrance to memory - I knew how quickly it would be replaced by the smell of dirt and sweaty, stinky feet.

"The question is, will they want to spend more time with you?" Ken wondered, sealing the box that now held all my pots and pans and the contents of the silverware drawer. He glanced over to make sure I knew he was kidding, and I stuck my tongue out. Mellow, upbeat, and hard working, my husband of 11 years liked to go with the flow, while I was a control freak prone to sarcasm and an occasional petty temper tantrum.

"Seriously," he said, "you've been working so much lately. Don't you think being a full-time mom will be a nice change?"

"I guess." Sarah, done cuddling, slid off my lap and headed into the living room. I watched her with a mother's acumen, calculating from her expression and gait that she'd be sleepy in fifteen to eighteen minutes. Mike, parked in front of the television in the living room, was like his dad - clever, easy going, and calm. When I'd asked him what he thought about moving, he said, "Will I be able to visit Uncle Rob and Aunt Lisa and the rest of the family?" I assured him he would and he shrugged and said, "Sounds cool."

Naturally the winter of '92 was one of the worst in Rhode Island's recent history. A native of New Jersey who'd spent time in Boston, I was used to a harsh climate, but this was ridiculous. The snow came early and hung around for months, soiled and ugly, like my mood.

One morning Sarah awoke listless and with a fever. If we lived in New Jersey the decision to pop her in the car and take her to the pediatrician would have been a no-brainer. But in this God-forsaken state, the closest pediatrician who was accepting new patients was 40 minutes away. I tried to get her to drink some juice, but she refused. I held her, rocked her, and my hand never left her forehead. Finally I called Ken and said I was taking her in, and would call him when we got home.

"She's fine," the pediatrician said. "Just a fever of unknown origin."

I held her in my lap. Silent and drowsy, not like my Sarah at all. "Unknown origin?" I repeated.

"Nothing to worry about. Just keep your eye on her and alternate Tylenol and Motrin every four and six hours."

Dismissed, I carried her out. Mike led the way, pressing the down button on the elevator, watching me, gauging my concern level. We got to the car and I strapped Sarah in. Even though Mike assured me he was old enough to do his own seatbelt, I checked it, then got in front.

"We'll go home and have lunch," I said with forced cheer, meeting his eyes in the rear view mirror. "This is a good day for hot soup and a peanut butter sandwich, isn't it?"

"Uh huh."

I left the parking lot and was back on the highway when Mike said, "Mom! Sarah is acting funny!"

"What do you mean, funny?" I tried to look at her without jeopardizing my driving. "What is she doing?"

"She's jumping and her head is shaking!"

I pulled over and turned around. To my horror, Sarah was having a seizure. "Sarah! Sarah!" I shouted, but she didn't respond. I drove back to the clinic and ran in with her in my arms, so scared I was crying. I told the receptionist that I needed to see the pediatrician again right away, and by the time he came out a minute later, the seizure had stopped. We went back into his office and while he examined her, she smiled as if nothing had happened.

"We'll run some tests," he said, "but I think it was a febrile seizure brought on by an extended fever. If the fever spikes again, apply cold face cloths to her skin, or give her a bath in cool water. That'll bring the fever down."

"But..."

"Meanwhile, let's see what the tests show."

His reassurance did nothing to calm me; on the contrary, I wondered if he even knew what he was talking about. Still frantic, I called Ken half an hour later, updated him, and said we were headed home. He said he'd leave work and meet us there.

"Okay, Mike, let's go." We got back into the elevator, headed down.

"Is Sarah going to die?" he asked in a scared little voice.

"No, honey! She's going to be just fine." He didn't object when I ruffled his hair, something he'd been saying lately that he was too big for. Holding Sarah tight, I forced myself to breathe.

"How is she?" Ken asked as soon as he came in. Sarah, sitting in my lap, reached for him. He picked her up and kissed the side of her head with a loud *mmm-WHAA!* that made her laugh.

"She seems fine. We'll get the results in a few days."

Handing her back to me, he put his hand on Mike's shoulder. "How you doing, buddy?"

"Good."

"Taking care of your mom?"

"Uh huh."

"Good boy."

The next day the fever returned, and it lasted for two days, despite the medication, compresses and cool baths. Terrified, I brought her back to the pediatrician, and once again she started seizing in the backseat of the car. But as soon as we got to the office she stopped. This went on for weeks, with trips back and forth to the hospital, a spinal tap, a chest x-ray, and to top everything off, an allergic reaction to some randomly-prescribed antibiotics. I didn't sleep for the entire month of March.

Then one afternoon I noticed that she seemed to have extra energy, playing with several toys at once. My hand went automatically to her forehead and she paused in her activity - a routine that had become familiar to us both. No fever! Grinning, she said, "Hi, Mommy!" as if she'd been away and was now back. After a big supper, she played some more, and asked Ken to read her a story.

The next day she was fine, and the next and the next. After a week I felt myself start to relax. Whatever she'd had was gone.

"Maybe Rhode Island made her sick," I told Ken. "It's so depressing here. I think gray is the state color."

"Maybe listening to you complain all the time made her sick," he joked. At least I chose to believe he was joking.

"I don't do that! Much."

"Well anyway, she's back to normal. Be happy."

I was glad to see Mike becoming friendly with some of the neighborhood kids, but had trouble getting used to the small town attitude of their mothers. Of everyone, for that matter. So different from what I was used to! One day I was browsing in a charming shop in Wickford, and happened to mention to the owner that Ken worked in Lincoln. "How far is Lincoln from Providence?" I asked. She said she thought it was pretty close. "How close?" I asked. She smiled. "I don't know, honey, I've never been to Providence."

Finally one morning brought a gorgeous display of magnolias and dogwoods; pink and white instead of gray. Ken was in the shower, the kids were still asleep, and as I stood looking out the window, I was humbled by the sudden realization that if I hadn't had such a bad winter, I wouldn't be feeling such awe and gratitude. They say that you can't have the good without the bad, and in that moment I "got" it. When Ken emerged from the bathroom he was greeted with my bright smile. "Everything is going to be fine," I said.

He kissed me. "I never doubted it."

That evening he came home to giddy stories about being outside; a picnic, a swing set, a sandbox, fresh air and sunshine. "We didn't even go inside almost at all!" Mike said.

"How was your day?" I eventually remembered to ask.

"Not as good as yours, but I did find out that another rep, this guy John I'm friendly with, is being transferred to Rhode Island too."

"Where's he from?"

"California."

"Wow. Culture shock."

"He and his wife Joanne have a son Mike's age. When they get here, let's have them over."

"Okay - meeting another transplant might be fun."

The minute I saw Joanne I knew that we were going to be friends. My age, with ash blonde hair, she was tall and large boned; not stick figure thin like the typical California girl. John seemed nice too, and while their son Eric played in the backyard with Mike, we engaged in grownup chat that broke off into men discussing work and sports, and women talking personal lives. Like me, she'd been traumatized by the move.

"It's not so bad, you'll get used to it," I said with gracious dishonesty. "At least you weren't here for the winter."

"Yeah, but summer here is not going to be like summer in California."

"I guess we'll see." I opened a bottle of wine and poured her a glass. "The hardest thing for me was leaving my family. I'm really close to my brother, Rob." I sipped. "He has AIDS."

"Oh!" She was startled by the announcement. "How is he?"

"Actually, he's doing great. He was diagnosed six years ago."

"Wow, that's a long time."

"I know, the doctors are really impressed. He says he's going to be the first to beat it. And he might, too, his body is responding to the medication. To look at him, you'd never know he's sick."

"Does he work?"

"He owns a dessert catering company. He makes the most beautiful pastries. Like something you'd see on a magazine cover. And taste like nothing else on this earth, you just can't imagine."

With dread I waited for her to say what everyone said: *"He has AIDS and he prepares food?"* But she grinned. "Let me know when he visits. I'll stop by with a doggie bag."

We grilled chicken and veggies, and Joanne brought a huge salad with stuff I never thought to incorporate, like walnuts and mandarin oranges. As mother to a little boy, she was enchanted by Sarah who was a girl through and through - pink and sweet and a master at the art of crying in order to get her way. Mike and Eric, just a few months apart in age, eyed one another shyly, and within a few minutes were playing like old pals; later exchanging secret, mirthful grins that led us to believe they'd participated in mischief somewhere, although they denied it and we never found anything amiss.

As evening cooled the air, we went inside. Ken took John into his office to show him the latest sales projections, and Joanne and I settled the kids by the TV, then opened another bottle of wine and sat in the dining room.

"I'm so glad you moved here," I said. "It'll be so great to have a friend! Until now I haven't had any other women to talk to. Not that I don't love talking baby talk all day."

"I know, I get so tired of the little cars and the little fighting men and those horrible cartoons. They seem so stupid. Were cartoons stupid when we were kids?"

"No! Remember that boy with the smart dog who wore glasses...Sherman and Peabody."

"Oh I loved them. What about that little turtle who traveled through time?"

"Oh yeah, that was good, you got to learn about other cultures and stuff! What about *Johnny Quest?*"

"And *The Jetsons?*"

"I used to love *Kimba the White Lion*," I admitted.

She said, "Yeah," nodded, then laughed. "Okay, *Kimba the White Lion* was a little stupid."

"We had so much fun, thanks for having us over," Joanne finally said at around 10:00. "I hope we didn't overstay our welcome."

"Can Eric spend the night, Mom?" Mike asked boldly. Delighted, I told him next time. Hugs were distributed, and I closed the door with a happy sigh.

Joanne and John rented a house near the ocean - coming from California, she had insisted upon that - and Ken and I had a large built-in pool. Stay-at-home moms, we spent most days that summer either at her house or mine. Life became even less complicated in the fall when they bought the house across the street, and more often than not we coordinated with our husbands and had supper together, usually barbeque. It became a joke - whose house were we eating at that night?

The fifteenth of November was Meg's 33rd birthday, and I followed up my card with a phone call, relishing as always that she was more than a year older than me. But she didn't respond to my teasing with her usual wry remarks.

"You okay?"

"I have a lot on my mind," she said. Unlike me, she could never launch into serious discussion, she always sort of hinted around and got you to probe before she could fully open up.

"Is everything okay?"

"I guess so."

"Are you sure?"

"Well..."

"How is Patrick?"

"He's good. We've been talking to doctors."

"About what?"

"Artificial insemination."

"Whoaa... really?"

"Yes, we've been trying to get pregnant for so long, Laur. I'm convinced my eggs are covered in mucous. I took a bunch of tests."

But you're so frail! I wanted to say. With her mucous-clogged lungs, she had trouble breathing even on the best of days. I didn't know her husband Patrick that well, but what was he thinking? Anyone could see she wasn't strong enough.

"Are you sure you want to do this?" I finally asked.

"I'm not sure of anything except that I want a baby."

"What about adopting?"

"We talked about it, but we want our own child if possible. The doctor seems to think that getting pregnant won't be a problem. It's whether or not I can go full term."

Everything inside me knew it was a bad idea. But I could tell from her tone that there'd be no talking her out of it. I could understand her desire for a child, I'd felt the same way my whole life, had always pictured myself a wife and mother. But pregnancy could - would - compromise her health. *Don't let her do this*, my gut said. And I always listened to my gut. Or at least always wished I did when I didn't.

"Meg," I said, "I believe that the reason some people can't get pregnant is because there's a child out there who needs them, and who wouldn't find them if they were able to have their own. Does that make sense?"

"Yes, but we want our own," she said, impatient; obviously hoping for a different reaction, like *Oh yes! Artificial insemination is perfect for you!* And I was tempted to do that for her, give her what she wanted. But I loved her too much, and was too worried.

"Most people feel that way until they see the baby, and then they go nuts. They love it just as if it was their own, and ..."

"I *said* we talked about it and decided we didn't want to do it," she interrupted.

I couldn't let her do it, but I couldn't stop her. *Think think...* "What about if I have the baby for you?" I heard myself say.

There was shocked silence on the other end, then she said, "What?"

"It would be yours and Patrick's baby, but I would carry it."

"What do you mean? How?"

"Like a surrogate mother. People do it all the time."

"So I would... you would... it would be my egg... or yours?"

"Yours. And Patrick's, you know, DNA."

"So Patrick and I would... we would be the true parents?"

"Of course! I would just carry the fetus for nine months. But it would come from you and Patrick."

"Oh Laurie! Do you think we could?"

"We should at least look into it. Don't you think?"

"I don't know what to think! Oh my God! Would you really... you would really do it for me?"

"Of course! How hard can it be?"

Getting excited, she said, "Okay, let's look into it! I'm going to ask my doctor if there are any clinics around that do that."

"I'll go to the library and do some research. We need to know as much as possible about it."

"Okay! Oh Laurie, I never thought about doing it this way!" she said. "You're the best and most amazing friend I ever had!"

"I haven't done anything yet," I joked.

"But you're offering. That's so great!"

"I'm sure you'd do it for me."

"Okay, let's do some research and talk tomorrow."

"Okay. I love you!"

"I love you too!"

I hung up feeling wonderful. Blessed to maybe be able to bestow the most miraculous gift upon one of my dearest friends. I wondered how Ken would react.

Questions

"Who were you on the phone with for so long?" Ken asked as I sat next to him on the couch.

I reached over and rubbed his shoulder. "Meg."

He melted into my massage. "How is she?" he asked, eyes shutting.

"Well..." I adjusted my position and used two hands, concentrating on his lower neck. Deep and intense, the way he liked it. "Imagine how I would be if I couldn't have kids."

He opened his eyes. "What?"

I explained their situation and told him about conversations she and I had when we were teens about having kids. So young, so sure we could do, be, have whatever we wanted. "We even came up with names. I remember that she wanted a daughter to call Isabella because she thought it sounded exotic."

"Must be hard for them."

"And they don't want to adopt, they want their own." I sighed, sat back, glanced at him. "So I was trying to come up with a way to help them. Don't forget, Meg and I have been friends for almost 20 years."

"Yeah."

"Longer than I've known you."

"Uh huh."

Thinking the conversation was over, he reached for the remote.

"Um, so I did sort of come up with an idea," I said.

"Oh?"

"I offered to have a baby for her."

Silence. I waited while he digested my words, a ponderous process that kept me in suspense for 30 long seconds.

"Wait," he said. "What?"

"I offered to carry the baby for her. Be a surrogate."

"Be pregnant with someone else's baby? For nine months?"

I nodded. "Yes."

"You just now told her you would do that?"

"Of course not! I told her I would talk to you first. More or less."

"Well... I mean... have you really given it any thought before now, or did you just offer spur of the moment?"

"Offered spur of the moment," I admitted. "But we talked about it a lot. And we're going to do a ton of research."

"Is it something you really want to do?"

"Yes." When he didn't respond, I added, "She sounded so sad. And we're so lucky to have Mike and Sarah. Doing this for Meg feels so right. You know?"

"It's so sudden!"

"Do you hate the idea?"

"I don't know. I don't think I hate it. I'm worried that you haven't thought the whole thing through. I mean, it's got to be more involved than you think."

"We're just in the beginning stages of it," I said. "Of course there are a lot of details to be discussed."

"But you're really willing to do this for her?"

"Yes."

"The nausea, the weight gain, the constipation, the needing to pee all the time? It won't bother you to go through it again?"

"No, I can do it. I want to do it for her."

He studied me for what felt like an hour, then looked past me, deep in thought, for what felt like another hour.

"Well?" I demanded.

"What if I said I didn't want you to do it?"

"Are you saying that?"

"No. But what if I did?"

"I already promised Meg."

"So it doesn't matter what I think, does it?"

"Of course it matters!" I slipped onto his lap, knowing I had won. "I wouldn't do it unless you approved." I kissed him on the cheek, then on the lips. "If you said *No* I would figure something out." His arm went around me. "Well I hope she appreciates what a friend she has in you. To be willing to do this!"

"I'm sure she appreciates it."

"And you're *sure*?"

"I'm sure I want to look into it."

"Okay."

I kissed him again, grateful, passionate. "I hope Sarah marries a man as wonderful as you."

"No one is as wonderful as me." He stroked my waist.

"I wish it wasn't so late, I'd call Rob. He's going to be so excited!"

"Why don't you wait until you know for sure it's really going to happen first before you tell anyone?"

"Well... okay."

I was right, Rob thought it was a great idea. "As long as you're sure you're up for it, physically."

"No sweat."

"Emotionally?"

"I'm fine."

"Not going to change your mind at the last minute and

want to keep it?"

I laughed. "No, thanks!"

"Then I say go for it!"

"What do you think Mom will say?"

"She'll be all for it, she's always loved Meg. Lisa too. But once you start telling everyone, be prepared for a million questions. That's why I kept my HIV status to myself for so long. As soon as people found out, they wanted constant updates. It was exhausting."

"Now that you mention it, how are you feeling?"

"Overwhelmed. Gearing up for Thanksgiving."

"Dad coming down to help you?"

"Yeah, for a few days." He sighed. "Which actually makes life harder, not easier. Working out the schedule so that he and Mom aren't in the same room at the same time."

"Ugh." When my dad ended the marriage 7 years ago by taking up with my mother's brother's ex-wife, the relationship went from horrible to really *really* horrible. They were definitely happier apart, but she'd never forgiven him, and they rarely spoke. "Good luck!"

"Thanks. Hey, maybe you and Ken and the kids can visit."

"I don't think you want Sarah running around your kitchen!"

"Nah, she'd be great. She and Mike could taste test everything."

"I'm sure you have plenty of people to volunteer for that job," I said, and we both laughed. "So apart from being too busy, you're okay?"

"Yeah, I'm fine. Saw the doctor last week. He said I shouldn't take on so many orders this year, but I can't say no. Oh, I have this new pumpkin cheesecake recipe, wait'll you taste it, you'll drop dead, I swear."

"Send me one!"

"What are your plans for Thanksgiving?"

"Joanne and John and Eric are coming over. I ordered a nineteen-pound turkey. Do you think that's too big?"

"Not if you invite, like, ten more people over. Hey, Lisa is here and she wants to talk to you, then I'll put Mom on. I'll let you tell them the news."

I heard my sister ask, *"What news?"* and the sound of the phone being transferred. "What news?" she asked me.

"Meg is going to be meeting with a surrogate mother so that she and Patrick can have a baby," I said.

"Oh that's great!"

"Guess who the surrogate mother is?"

There was silence, then Lisa chuckled. "Gee, let me think, Laur. You?"

"What do you think?"

"I think it's amazing! It's so great that you're willing to do that!"

Already I was uncomfortable with people dwelling on what I was doing. It didn't feel like such a big deal, and I kept wanting to say *Meg would do it for me!* "Not like I'm donating a kidney, you know," I said. "Remember how easy my pregnancies were?"

"Yeah, but still! Hey, Mom is trying to pry the phone away from me, let me put her on..."

My mother and I talked for a while, and like Rob and Lisa, she loved the surrogacy idea. As soon as I hung up with her, the phone rang, and Meg said, "Hi, whatcha doin?" in a cheery voice.

"Oh, Meg, my family thinks it's great that we're doing this!"

"You told your family already?"

"Of course!"

"I haven't told anyone but Patrick yet."

"Not even your mom?"

"No, Laurie. We thought it was smarter to wait until we find out what's involved. We don't even know if we can do it."

"Well I'm only going to tell Rob, my mother, my dad, Lisa, Joanne, and Ken's brother and sister in law. But no one else."

"It's just that it's private. I don't want to have to do a lot of explaining."

"Okay. Hey, Meg, Ken and I were talking, and we think the four of us should get together after we get all the information from doctors and stuff. I've only met Patrick at your wedding, and he and Ken have never met. If we're going to do this, we should have a face to face and iron out all the details."

"I think so too. Patrick and I are driving to Georgia to visit my mother at the end of December. We can stop in Rhode Island on our way back."

"Maybe you could be here for New Years!"

"Oh that would be fun! Let's talk later. I have calls in to some clinics and don't want to tie up the line in case they're trying to get through. I'll let you know if I find out anything."

"Okay! Love you."

"Love you too."

The day before Christmas I packed up pillows and PJs and we hurried across the street to Joanne's. Hanukkah was fun, but Christmas was festive, with more glitz; lights, camera, action.

"You say that because you don't have to spend six hours putting up decorations and then three hours a month later taking them down and putting them back in the attic," Joanne said as I admired her display of nutcrackers, and the beautiful hand-made ornaments on her tree. She and Eric had even strung popcorn and cranberries.

"All I know is, it looks gorgeous in here." I pulled Sarah away from the stack of presents. "Not yet, honey."

"I'm just about to have eggnog. Want some?"

"Sure."

"I was going to put rum in it. Is that okay?"

"Very okay." I got Sarah settled with a toy, asked Mike to keep an eye on her, and followed Joanne into the kitchen. Ken and John, both working, had promised to get home early.

"I wasn't sure if you were abstaining from alcohol," she said, pulling out two grinning pink-cheeked Santa mugs.

"Not until I'm pregnant."

"I've been so busy getting ready for Christmas that I haven't had a chance to ask what's the latest?"

"Still in the research stage. There's a lot to know, but not much literature out there. I mean, it's almost 1994! You'd think there'd be articles and stuff. But information is kinda hard to find. Meg's spoken to doctors, I've just made trips to the library."

"What do the doctors say?"

"That there's no reason we shouldn't try. It means lots of tests and shots and getting our bodies ready." She handed me my eggnog. I sipped. "God, this is so good. Don't let me have another one, even if I beg."

"Okay." We went back into the living room. She put on a tape of Christmas music and lowered the lights so we could enjoy the twinkling tree." You must be psyched about seeing Meg."

"I am. I can't wait for you to meet her!"

"I feel like I already have, I've heard so much about

her. But don't feel you need to invite me over; you guys have a lot to discuss."

"Silly. I have plenty of time for you both."

"As long as I'm there when you have the baby!"

"Don't worry, you're the first person I'll call - I'll need you to come over and watch the kids."

Our gaze automatically went to the three of them sitting near the presents, sneaking peeks at tags, eyes sparkling with innocent excitement. One of those warm, peaceful moments that has everything to do with family and gratitude.

Ken and John surprised us by getting home earlier than we expected, and took the boys out to build a snowman. Sarah, content to sit on the floor playing with Tupperware, felt like she was helping Joanne and me in the kitchen. After dinner we parked the kids in front of the TV to watch Christmas cartoons, and got a game of poker going. Laughed a lot, drank a little, kept the language clean, drank a little more, joked that it was a good thing we only lived across the street.

Meg and Patrick arrived the day before New Year's, which was also Ken's birthday. Meg looked radiant as she hugged me. Patrick presented me with a huge bouquet of yellow roses, and shook hands with Ken as introductions were made. Inside, Mike and Sarah, shy at first, grew more interested when Meg showed them pictures of her dog, a beautiful lab named Finn. We had a few pizzas delivered and passed the evening chatting and catching up. Once the kids went to bed, we got a little more serious, discussing the information we'd been able to find, until Meg yawned and said she was exhausted from the long drive. By 10:00 we were all asleep.

The next day was New Year's Eve. Meg and I cooked, twice sent Ken and Patrick and the kids to the store for something we needed. Late in the afternoon Joanne, John and Eric came over. Mike and Eric gleefully secured permission to stay up and watch the ball drop in Times Square, but conked out before 11:00. Joanne and Meg and I engaged in girl talk - giggling and making fun of our husbands, then saying *"Nothing!"* when they asked what was so funny. At midnight everyone kissed everyone else.

Patrick and Meg wanted to take Ken out for his birthday the next evening, so I asked Joanne if she'd babysit. We went to an Italian place, and after the waitress took our drink orders and walked away, Meg said to me, "Maybe soon you'll just be having water with dinner."

"I hardly ever drink, but the doctor told me that an occasional glass of wine while you're pregnant isn't bad. Relaxes you. I had a few during my pregnancies."

"Really?" She sounded skeptical.

"I won't if you don't want me to. I'm just telling you what the doctor said. I mean, I had a few glasses of wine when I was carrying Mike, and he turned out okay. Don't you think?" I saw her glance at Patrick, and said again, "I won't if you don't want me to. It's your pregnancy. I am at your service."

"I don't want you to feel like you can't do something if you want to do it. I don't want you to feel like you're my slave."

"Don't be silly. It doesn't matter to me. I'll do whatever you and Patrick feel comfortable with. I'm glad you said something. We shouldn't keep anything from each other. If something is bothering one of us, we need to talk about it. If we're worried, angry, happy or whatever. Okay? This won't work unless we're totally honest with each other."

"I agree."

"And that goes for the husbands, too," Patrick said. "I mean, we're here to talk about the nitty gritty, but we don't even know what the nitty gritty is."

"I sort of feel that way too," Ken put in. "We don't have all the facts yet. How can we plan and make choices?"

"Men!" I said. "Everything has to be so concrete and in front of you! I think the emotional component is what's important right now. We should discuss all the scenarios and see how we'd feel if any of them happened. Explore our reactions and be prepared for disasters. For example, I wanted to ask you, Meg, how do you think you'll be able to handle not being pregnant while I am?"

"What do you mean?"

"Well if I knew I wasn't going to be able to carry a child, I'd be sad."

"You would? Why?"

"Because I mean, I would feel like I was missing out on a lot of the actual experience. And I don't want you to feel bad about it. I wonder if you should, sort of, mourn your loss before we go through with this?"

"My loss?" She glanced at Patrick again, this time perplexed.

"I mean by doing this you're like...um... you're conceding that you couldn't do it on your own, and so... I mean, do you know what I mean?"

"I guess I've already gone through these emotions. It's part of having CF all my life, I've always had to accept my limitations. I feel fine."

"I guess what I'm saying is, it would be perfectly normal to be sad. And you should feel free to let me know if you are. And I will tell you that you're not missing out on anything. I know some women are never so happy and beautiful as when they're pregnant, but I wasn't like that at all. My skin was a mess, I was the size of a house and clumsy and bulky, and there was no sex at all."

"None," Ken concurred.

"I won't be sad," Meg said.

"I still say we should begin the process first," Ken said. See if it's going to work, before we delve into all the psychological implications."

The waitress returned with our drinks, took our meal orders, and left again.

"I agree with Ken," said Patrick, "but if we're going to talk about emotions, what about you? How will you feel about giving up a baby you've carried for nine months?"

"Fine," I said. "No problem at all."

"Ken?"

"Same. No problem."

"But how can you be sure? What if you see the baby and you fall in love and all of a sudden you can't give it away?"

"I know that won't happen. I know myself, I know for a fact that I don't want another kid. Also, I didn't bond with Mike or Sarah until they were about three days old. Believe me, it wasn't love at first sight with me!" I turned to Ken. "Remember when the nurse came back with Mike and asked if I wanted to hold him, and I just said, *'No thanks, maybe tomorrow.'*

"The shocked look on her face!" Ken laughed.

I laughed too, and went on, "Most important, Patrick, I won't feel like the baby is mine because it won't be. Biologically it's Meg's egg and your sperm. I'm just the suitcase."

"Okay, let me ask you this - are you going to be okay with so many people in the delivery room? It's such a private thing."

"Of course. That's not even on my radar screen of

things to worry about."

"What *is* on your screen?"

"Well, Ken and I have talked about how our kids will react. Sarah is too young, but Mike will be in school, and one of my concerns is how he'll tell people what his mom is doing. Another concern is, how do I act when people ask about the baby?"

"Meg and I would rather you not tell anyone what you're doing," Patrick interrupted. "Just pretend it's yours."

I stared. "Pretend it's mine? What happens if I run into someone a few months later? They'll want to know where it is."

"This is a personal matter. I'm not comfortable with a million people knowing."

"I understand that it's personal," I said, "but no one knows you in Rhode Island. And it's my privacy that's being invaded here, not yours. People don't have to know I'm a surrogate for you, but I'd like them to know I'm a surrogate for a friend. Otherwise I'm left carrying a child, pretending it's mine, and then concocting some story nine months later about why I don't have it anymore."

"What Patrick means," Meg said, "is that the fewer people who know, the better. Don't tell anyone unless they ask."

"That's just it. When you're pregnant, people *do* ask. They even touch. And I can't just say *'It's none of your business.'* That seems so rude to me." I looked at Meg. "I'm at least going to tell Mike's teacher, so she can be aware of any situations that arise at school because of it." Sipping my wine, I tried to figure out how I would feel if I were on the other side of this; tried to justify their need for secrecy. Meg never minded telling people she had CF. Why be uptight now? Battling annoyance, I took another sip of wine and wished someone would say something that made sense.

"Laurie," Meg spoke up just as the silence became unbearable for me, "what's the best part about this for you?"

"Being able to give you something you've always wanted," I said. "Seeing you happy."

She smiled, her old self. "I want you to know how much we appreciate this. Even if it doesn't happen, if it isn't possible or doesn't work... that you were willing to do it means a lot to Patrick and me."

"A lot," Patrick agreed.

Our food arrived and we spent the next hour eating and chatting about everything but what we were there to talk about. When our desserts arrived I brought up the subject again.

"You asked me what would be the best part of this, but you didn't ask what the worst part will be."

"What will it be?"

"Living so far apart. Visiting won't be easy while I'm pregnant, and we won't get to see the baby growing up and I won't get to see you be a mommy."

"Actually," Patrick said, "that's probably a good thing."

For a second I thought I misunderstood. "How is that a *good thing*?"

"It'll be better for Meg if she's doing this on her own, without you. Then it will really be our child. Our responsibility."

"Of course it'll be yours! I'm not going to interfere, I didn't mean that at all!"

"No, I know. But if you're far away, she won't feel, I don't know, obligated to call you about every detail."

Obligated to call me? I didn't look at anyone as I finished my dessert.

The Application

A few days into the new year Meg called to tell me about her appointment with a specialist. "He was great, Laur! He put me in contact with the Organization of Parents Through Surrogacy."

"Oh, I've been reading about the OPTS. They recommend eliminating any clinic that can't provide a 21% success rate."

"Right. Hey, he was sort of concerned about your mental stability."

"He was? How come?"

"He had trouble understanding why someone, even a good friend, would be willing to sacrifice so much for no money. He said probably a lot of people will find it hard to believe you just want to do this out of the goodness of your heart."

"Who cares! They'll see when I hand the baby over with no regrets."

"It's just that it *is* a huge thing to do. It affects your life, your health, your family. Patrick and I have to be absolutely sure you want to do it before we go any further."

"I want to do it," I said. "I'm absolutely sure."

"The other thing is, the doctor hasn't ruled out Patrick and me going through invitro fertilization on our own."

"Oh?"

She sighed. "I don't know what to do. If you hadn't offered to do this, of course we'd try. But it's not fun and it's not cheap, and what if it doesn't work? Doing it with you seems like a better route."

"Well," I said, "you know how I feel about the risk of you carrying a baby. But I'm not going to tell you what to do. You and Patrick will have to make this decision on your own."

"I know."

"I wouldn't, though, Meg. It's so dangerous for you."

She laughed. "Thanks for not telling me what to do, Laur!"

I awoke the next day with a ferocious sinus headache. Sarah was her absolute worst, screaming and fussing and wouldn't eat or do anything I asked. Four tantrums before noon and my whole body hurt. "I will give you the stuffed animal of your choice if you will go to sleep!" I shouted, frustrated and on the verge of tears. When she finally settled down for a nap, I lay on the couch, miserable, feverish, shivering, and throat sore. Was I really up for the crabbiness, the mood swings, the general feeling of crap? The weight gain? The stress on my system, managing a house and kids? Being pregnant with Sarah when Mike was three had been challenging. Could I handle being pregnant with Mike *and* Sarah? Sarah wasn't exactly easy the way Mike had been.

What if I'd made the offer impulsively, and then convinced myself I wanted to do it? Meg was right: I had to decide before we went any further with it. Mind buzzing, I dozed until Sarah's next tantrum began an hour later.

"Trust me when I say there's no danger of me

changing my mind and keeping Meg's baby," I said to Ken
when he came home that night with Chinese food so I
wouldn't have to cook. "I'm even having second thoughts
about keeping Sarah."

He smiled. "Everything is overwhelming when you're
sick. As soon as you feel better you'll be back to your old
powerhouse self."

He was right. By the time Meg called that weekend, I
was excited to hear that she and Patrick had decided to
proceed with my surrogacy services.

"I'm having a package sent to you full of information
about the actual procedure. No offense, but it sounds like all
the clinics require that you go through psychological testing."

"At last, the chance to prove I'm sane!"

"No comment."

"Do you and Patrick have to be evaluated too?"

"No."

"Oh." Was I the only one who was concerned about
her feelings? Yes, she'd be getting a baby. But what about
deeper emotions; what about feelings of inadequacy? What if
she didn't bond with the baby since she hadn't carried it?
What if she wound up resenting it for what it represented - her
failure to conceive like a "normal" woman? Why was no one
else asking these questions? I broke our rule and decided not
to be honest about it. "Hey, want to talk tonight after the rates
go down?"

"No, I can't wait that long. Guess what? There's a
surrogacy lawyer in Rhode Island!"

"There is? Where?"

"North Kingston. Is that near you?"

"Yes, it's about fifteen minutes away! Of course in
Rhode Island everything is fifteen minutes away. Did you call
him?"

"No, it's on my To Do list. I'll let you know as soon

as I do. Okay?"

"Okay!"

Two hours later she called back. "The lawyer's name is Mitchell Galvin. He walked me through the process and I feel so much better about everything. He told me about a clinic in Delaware that has a 50% success rate!"

"Wow, that's really high!"

"I know, I'm going to check them out. Oh, he also gave me the name of a psychologist who can test you. I'll give you the number and you can call and make an appointment."

"Okay."

"Plus don't you think you should make an appointment with your OBGYN? Make sure he can deal with this."

"Okay. Hey, Meg, I was thinking, we're spending so much time on the phone, maybe you should get an 800 number."

"An 800 number?"

"Yeah. I did a little research. You can get one on a temporary basis, and the rates are less. We can talk a lot more often. My phone bills are astronomical and we've only been at this for two months."

"Maybe," she said. "Okay, here's the number for the psychologist."

I wrote it down, thanked her, and hung up feeling uneasy; I was the only one going under a microscope.

"You'll be fine," Ken said. "Just act sane. Want me to go with you?"

"Are you kidding? I'd love it!"

"They're not going to try to determine if *I'm* sane, right?"

I laughed, kissed him. "No, we won't be there long enough."

"So you think I'm doing the right thing?" I asked Joanne the next day. "Everyone is being so supportive; but sometimes I think everyone is saying *'She's nuts!'* behind my back, and no one wants to be the one to tell me."

"Are you kidding? I think what you're doing is fantastic and brave. Are you having second thoughts?"

"I don't know."

"If you don't know, then you must be."

"Maybe." I sipped my coffee and tilted my head to hear if Sarah was up yet; satisfied that she was still napping, I went on, "I guess it's one thing to talk about it. But then to actually do it... I have to be honest with myself - I'm kinda nervous about being pregnant again. I was all set in my mind that I was done with that."

"Maybe you just need to get used to the idea."

"Maybe. The other thing is, I feel weird about talking to Dr. Stoller, my OBGYN. I've only met him once, and I wasn't planning on having any babies with him, so to speak. I have an appointment with him next week. Can you watch Sarah?"

"Of course."

"Thanks."

She reached over and put her hand on my arm. "Laurie, I'm sure it's normal to feel confused and scared."

"It's not just that," I said. "I hope that I'm not doing this as a distraction. To keep me from worrying about Rob."

"He's okay, isn't he?"

"He's fine."

"Do you think that's why you're doing this?"

I thought for a moment, then shook my head.

"I don't either," she said.

"And another thing..."

"Yes?"

"I want to eat really well this time, and be in really good shape. I was in okay shape when I was pregnant with my kids, but I didn't really go out of my way to eat healthy. I feel more responsible with this pregnancy because it's not my kid. Does that make sense?"

"Of course. Probably anyone going through this would feel like that. Too bad there aren't any books out there telling you what to expect, emotionally."

"Maybe when this is over and we're all living happily ever after, I can write one," I said.

As I told Dr. Stoller what Meg and I were planning to do, he listened closely, nodding, obviously intrigued.

"I have no experience with this kind of thing," he said, "but I don't see any reason why we can't do it. I'll order some blood tests to get us going, and when the results come in, I'll let you know."

"Sounds good."

"And you're sure you want to do this?"

"Yes. But one thing that concerns me a little is the cost."

"Does your insurance cover this kind of thing?"

"I don't know."

"Let me find out. I'll be discreet."

"Thanks, that would be great!"

"I'll be in touch, Laurie. And you keep me updated, too."

"I will. Thanks again." I left with a light heart,

relieved that he was going to be supportive. Another obstacle out of the way.

After five I called Meg and told her.

"I hope your insurance will cover it," she said. "That would save Patrick and me a ton of money."

"I'll let you know what he finds out."

"If it's not covered, we'll just have to deal with it, I guess."

"So what about you, did you find out what's involved for you?"

"Yes. I need a series of tests and shots before they can retrieve my eggs. Patrick can give me the shots at home, but the egg retrieval part makes me nervous. I wish the clinics here had the experience yours in the States have. IVF Canada hasn't had a single successful gestational surrogacy. But they've only been doing it since July. Two surrogates did get pregnant, but one miscarried and one had an ectopic. So it's not really fair to judge their success rate this early in the game."

"We should do it here, then."

"But all my doctors are here. If something went wrong..."

"Nothing will go wrong," I said. "But I agree. Do it there."

"Okay. Oh, I have your part of the application. I'll send it to you. Call me when you get it, okay?"

"Okay."

IVF Application Question for the Surrogate:
What made you decide to become a gestational carrier?

Answer: I was seriously concerned for the health and well being of my friend Meg, who has Cystic Fibrosis. We have thought this out very carefully and have had many discussions with our husbands, and all of us agree that it's what we want to do.

IVF Application Question for the Surrogate:
How would you describe yourself?

Answer: A loyal friend. A compassionate, caring person. A good mother. Honest and giving. Decent wife. Sincere, but maybe bitchy and sarcastic at times. Passionate and dedicated.

IVF Application Question for the Surrogate:
What do you think is the biggest stress in your life at present?

Answer: Money and the stress of now being a full-time mother of two instead of a part-time working mother of one. We moved recently and I don't like living so far away from my family. My brother Rob is seriously ill.

IVF Application Question for the Surrogate:
If you could write a message to the child born through your participation in the gestational surrogacy program for when he or she turns 18, what would you tell him or her?

Answer: Dear _____, I would never have been a surrogate for money or for a stranger. I offered this gift to your parents out of my love for them and my concern for your mother's health. I've known your mother for over 20 years and by the time you read this I will have known her for 38 years. Although distance has always separated us, our friendship has not diminished; in fact, it has grown over the years. Your parents wanted you so desperately, they were willing to risk your mom's health to have you. If that had happened, you never would have found out what a truly remarkable person she is. So I offered to do this, and your parents took the very courageous step to accept. This procedure in 1994 is still controversial (I hope by the time you read this in the year 2012 it will be more common) and you should feel blessed that your parents were willing to do this to have you. I am also blessed, to have them as friends. You are a miracle of science, and the product of a tremendous amount of love.

TO: IVF Canada
FROM: Doug Stoller, M.D.
RE: Laurie Miller
DATE: February 14, 1994

I have had the opportunity to examine Laurie Miller. Mrs. Miller is a very pleasant 34 year-old *Gravida II, Para II* female who presents for the possibility of surrogacy. Mrs. Miller has had a prior Cesarean section, which was followed by a successful VBAC. Currently Mrs. Miller is in good health. Her blood pressure is 108/66. She is 5 ft. 5 in. tall and weighs 140 lbs. Recently, we had blood drawn; enclosed is a copy of those lab results. Rubella is immune, CMV is negative, RPR is non-reactive. HIV is negative, Hepatitis-B surface antibody is negative, and herpes index HSV-1 is positive on TORCH antibody, and HSV-II is also positive via TORCH antibodies. If you have any questions, please feel free to contact me. In addition, if I can be of assistance to you in the surrogacy program with respect to Mrs. Miller, please give me specific instructions as to how you would like her to be stimulated and I would be happy to comply.

Sincerely,
Dr. Stoller, M.D.

Visitors

In February my mother, Lisa, and Rob drove up to celebrate Sarah's second birthday. Mike was at school, but Sarah and I met them at the door, waving as they got out of the car.

"Look!" I said, "it's Mom-Mom and Ti-Ti and Uncle Rob!"

Used to visiting them in New Jersey, Sarah was puzzled to see them in *her* yard. Then she pointed at them and looked up at me. "Oh!"

First to the porch, Mom hugged me, then crouched. "Hello, birthday girl!" Giggling, Sarah leapt into her arms. I hugged Lisa, then watched Rob climb the stairs, one hand on the railing, looking weary. I felt ribs as I hugged him. "I'm so glad you're here," I said. "Come on inside."

"Wow, this place is huge!" he said, looking around. Lisa had been there to help me move, but he and Mom were seeing it for the first time.

"Ken and I call it our grownup house." I steered everyone into the living room. "And the neighborhood is great."

"I like Cheerios," Sarah announced, and everyone laughed.

"A food connoisseur like her uncle," Rob said, scooping her up and giving her a big smack on the cheek. Then he set her down and tried to hold back a yawn. "Mind if I lie down for a few?"

"No, of course not." I grabbed his suitcase and led everyone up the stairs. Halfway down the hall Sarah insisted on showing them her room, which involved presenting all her favorite dolls and stuffed animals, one by one, handing them out and waiting for everyone to exclaim over them. A time-consuming process that required a lot of patience.

"Honey, let's get everyone settled in, then we can look at your toys."

"I wanna show them one more."

"Okay. One more." I gauged the room - no one seemed annoyed, but Rob had lowered himself onto a chair. "Show them Sally."

"No."

She looked through her toy box, somber and focused on making the right selection. At last she withdrew Sally, a wonderful handmade doll with blonde yarn hair, green and white striped pantaloons, and a purple beret. "Look!"

"Amazing!" pronounced Rob with a teasing grin, the one who'd given it to her the day she was born. He stood. "Where's my room?"

"I'll show you." Linking my arm through his, I escorted him down the hall to the last door on the left. "How are you, anyway?"

"Good. Working too many hours."

"Shouldn't you sort of take it easy?"

"I should. But I don't want to." He lay down and shut his eyes. "Not to kick you out, but bye."

"Don't beat around the bush, just say what's on your mind," I laughed. "See you in a bit?"

"Yeah, I just need a few minutes."

"Okay." I shut the door quietly as if he was already asleep; upset to see him so knocked out. In high school girls used to say *"Oh my God, that's your brother?"* as if it was unimaginable that someone so gorgeous could share my gene pool. Years later, when he told me he was gay, I was shocked.

Meg called that evening to let me know she'd gotten my OBGYN reports and application. "I'll add it to Patrick's and my stuff and send it to IVF Canada right away. As soon as they get everything they'll set up an interview, probably within two weeks."

"Okay." From the living room I heard animated conversation that included the kids, and shouts of laughter. Rob's voice as he played with Mike, and Sarah's shrieks - he had probably lifted her over his head. My mother's warning tone, and Ken's patient assurance - *"Don't worry, she's fine."* Taking a deep breath and with heart pounding, I said, "Hey, Meg? I need to tell you something."

"What?"

"Well, I was really upset by Patrick's comment that night at the restaurant, about it being a good thing that we live far apart."

"Oh Laurie, he didn't mean anything. That's just the way he is about this kinda stuff."

"You mean when people offer to carry his child? That's just the way he is?"

"No." She laughed. "I mean, like we told you, we're very private people."

"I have to be honest, I'm getting a little tired of the private people excuse."

"Well, I think what he meant was that when this is over, he wants to just move on with our lives."

"When this is over? Move on with your lives? You make it sound bad, like chemo or a heart transplant or something!" With effort I kept my voice low so no one could hear. "And I don't see it as being 'over.' It'll be just the beginning."

"Laurie, I know."

"I mean, do you feel that way? That if we have the baby we'll just go on our separate ways?"

"Of course not!"

"Good. Because that would kill me."

"You always overanalyze everything, and come up with the worst thing that could happen. Don't worry!"

"You're right, I'm just being neurotic."

"You are. So tell me how was Sarah's birthday, and how is Rob?"

Feeling better, I laughed. "Such a snob. He made fun of the cake I baked - from a mix, I didn't have time for scratch - and then had two pieces."

"Hey, don't knock the mixes! That's all I use. Well, I hear Patrick's car in the driveway, I have to get going."

"Okay, talk later."

"Wait... Laurie?"

"Yes?"

"Next time I call you, it'll be to say *Get your ass up here!*"

Sure enough, on March 6th I was on a plane headed to Toronto. Gazing out the window, I thought about baby names, baby shoes, and baby firsts, until we landed an hour later. I made my way through Customs, then spotted Meg waiting for me on the other side of the glass! *"Hi!"* I mouthed, and waved; a few minutes later we were in each other's arms.

"I'm so glad you're here! I can't believe we're going to do this!"

"Me too! Me either!"

We laughed and held each other for another moment.

Then she pulled away. "I do have some bad news," she said.

"What?"

"My dad has Non-Hodgkins Lymphoma."

"Oh no!"

"He found out yesterday."

"I'm so sorry! What did the doctor say?"

"He has to have chemo."

"Did you tell him what we're doing?"

"Of course not. I haven't told anyone but my mom."

"Oh Meg, you should tell him right away. It'll give him something good to think about while he's sick. That's why I told Rob right away."

"Maybe."

Meaning *No*. I knew her dad's illness was a lot for her to deal with and she didn't need me telling her what to do, so I left it alone. I had my way of handling things, and she had hers.

I was a little nervous about seeing Patrick again, but when he came home from work he greeted me with a tight hug.

"Good to see you," he said. "How are Ken and the kids?"

"Everyone is fine, thanks. They said to say hello."

"Tell them I said hello back." He kissed Meg then crouched to caress Finn, the dog, who was nagging for attention. I wondered if Meg had even mentioned to him that I'd been hurt by his comment. Didn't look that way. Thinking about it brought a fresh pang, but I pushed it aside.

The IVF Canada clinic was on the second floor of an unassuming office building, and nothing like the high-tech atmosphere I anticipated. Pictures of chubby, cuddly babies hung on the walls, and women in various stages of pregnancy occupied most of the chairs. Meg checked out every belly, and then whispered, "Just think, that could be you soon!"

"Us," I whispered back.

She and Patrick and I had no sooner sat down when we were approached by a middle-aged stocky woman with a pleasant smile. "Meg and Patrick and Laurie?"

"Yes," Patrick answered as the three of us stood.

"I'm Sue Davis, the clinic coordinator. We received your applications and everything looks in order. Laurie, have you scheduled an appointment with a psychologist?"

"Yes."

"Good. Nothing can proceed until that report is on file. Meanwhile, I'll walk you through our protocol, and take you on a tour. When we're done, you'll have a chance to sit with Dr. Lee and he'll explain the procedure in detail. Okay?"

We nodded. She led us up a winding staircase then down a hall, stopping at the first door on the right. "This is the lab, where egg meets sperm." Pushing open the door and stepping aside, she allowed us to peer at technicians hunched over slides and petri dishes like they were an exhibit at the zoo. "And here..." she said, leading us to the next room, "is where we keep the frozen embryos."

We saw ten metal cylinders that were about two feet in diameter and about three feet high. She turned the handle on one of them, and as the top opened, smoke from the liquid nitrogen billowed out. We almost knocked heads trying to look inside, and saw smaller test tubes inside that were about the size of cocktail straws. "Each tube holds the embryos of different clients; some clients have many tubes, some only one." She waited a second, then sealed the tank. "Meg, you and Patrick will have to decide what you want done with any embryos that are left over."

"What we want done with them?" Meg asked.

"Well, let's assume we retrieve eight eggs and we fertilize all eight. And let's assume that Laurie gets pregnant on the live attempt..."

"Live attempt?" Patrick interrupted.

"The first time the embryos haven't been frozen yet. We call them "live." So let's say she carries your baby to term. That leaves us with five or six frozen embryos. You can choose to keep them here in case you want them in the future. Or you can donate them to a couple who needs them. Or you can have them destroyed."

"Oh," said Meg. She glanced at Patrick, who was starting to look overwhelmed.

"I'm not sure what we'll do," he said.

Sue smiled. "You don't have to decide now. At some point you may need to though, so let's keep it in mind. Believe me, you'll be leaving here with a pile of brochures and paperwork!"

"Sounds like fun," I observed, glad I wasn't going to have to make any life-changing decisions and spend hours filling out forms.

Sue led us back up the hall, and delivered us to Dr. Lee's office. "I'm sure he'll be here soon."

"Thanks," Meg said.

"Good luck."

We watched her leave, sat, and in a few minutes a short, white-jacketed, smart-looking man in his 50s appeared. Everyone shook his hand, and then he gestured that we should sit again.

"First, let me explain that the procedure itself is very simple. We begin by giving Meg something to suppress her egg production. When Laurie starts her menstrual cycle, we'll give Meg something else, to stimulate egg production. That way your cycles are matched. Once Laurie ovulates, we'll remove Meg's eggs and fertilize them with Patrick's sperm. The embryos remain in the lab 24 to 48 hours, until they reach the eight-cell stage. Laurie will have a sonogram to determine if her uterine wall is thick enough to accept the embryos, and if it is, we implant them through her cervix."

"Piece of cake," I said.

"Have you decided how many embryos you'd like to try?"

The question took us all by surprise. "How many?" Patrick repeated on everyone's behalf.

"Normally we implant two to six. Some won't survive, so you like to plan for that by having extra. On the other hand, if they all take, you could wind up with sextuplets."

"Oh my God," said Meg.

"You don't have to decide this second, but you need to know before we do it."

"Okay," said Patrick. "So after the embryos are implanted, what happens next? We just... go home?"

Dr. Lee chuckled. "Basically. Laurie will have to stay for an hour or so, lying on a special tilting table that elevates the lower half of her body."

"What?" I said, "Why?"

"It's part of the procedure. Between us, I'm not sure there's sufficient evidence that it provides any benefits, but a lot of clients feel that if they stand up right away, the embryos will fall out."

"I usually go to the bathroom after sex, and I still got pregnant twice," I offered bluntly.

Dr. Lee smiled. "Plus this process uses considerably less fluid, so the chances of the embryos falling out are really almost non-existent. But as I say, clients seem to prefer lying inverted afterwards."

"Okay."

"Then what?" Meg asked.

"After implantation, we freeze the remaining embryos in case you need them. If you don't need them, you may wish to donate them."

"Sue explained all that," Patrick said. "And we probably won't donate them."

"We may need them to try again," Meg added quickly. "I guess the main question is, what are the chances that the baby could inherit my CF?"

"CF is a recessive disease, meaning a person has to inherit the gene mutation from both parents. Unless Patrick has the gene, the baby won't get it. You need to get tested. I'll give you the name of a genetic counselor."

"Okay, good," Patrick said.

Dr. Lee delivered a smile of finality. "Unless you have any other questions... ?"

"I think we're all set," Meg said with a look at Patrick, who nodded. "Thanks for explaining it to us."

"Appreciate it," Patrick said, as he and Dr. Lee stood at the same time and shook hands.

"The receptionist has more information for you. It's a lot to take in all at once. Go home, read the literature, make your appointments, and we'll be in touch."

We thanked him again and headed out, minds buzzing. There wasn't much conversation during the ride back to Meg and Patrick's house, but as soon as we sat down to lunch, we all started talking at once.

"We have to divide it into steps: what has to get done first, in order to progress to the next thing," I finally said in a good loud voice. "I have to get my psychological testing done, and Patrick has to be tested for the CF gene. Number one."

"Number two, we have to decide how many embryos to implant," Meg said. "I had no idea we'd be the ones to make that decision. It seems they should have some sort of standard number. Laurie, imagine you having six babies?"

"You guys need to decide how many babies you can take care of, realistically, and we can worry about me later." I took a bite of my sandwich, then the impact of what I'd just said hit me. "Whoa," I amended quickly. "I can't carry six babies!"

"Of course not," Meg said. "I could never take care of six kids. I have enough trouble taking care of me. Twins would be the most I could handle. And even then, I'd need help."

"Twins I can do," I said.

"So two embryos," Patrick said. "We agree?"

"Yes. Two," I said.

Meg looked at Patrick. "We have to decide about what do to with the frozen embryos if some are left over after Laurie gets pregnant."

"We'll talk about it, but I have some pretty strong feelings about what I want to do. And it's pointless to decide now, we should wait and see where we are in a few weeks. Laurie, your appointment is at the end of April?"

"Yes."

"So if that doctor can get the evaluation to IVF right away, and we have the genetic report done by then, we can start the process in June!"

"Oh my God, *June!*" Meg said, eyes sparkling.

"Perfect!" I said. "I'd much rather be pregnant in the fall and winter than the summer."

We all smiled, already thinking *when* not *if*.

I caught an early flight the next morning and was

home by 11:00. Joanne, who'd been babysitting Sarah, demanded to hear all the details. As I filled her in, I was suddenly exhausted from the intensity of the approaching reality, and all the information I'd had to absorb. After a quick lunch, Sarah and I picked up Mike from kindergarten, stopped at the supermarket to buy something for supper, then headed back home where I unpacked and did three loads of laundry, all the while listening to *The Lion King* soundtrack over and over. Supper was on the table when Ken came home at 6:00.

"Welcome home, I missed you!" he said, kissing me before turning to greet the kids, both of whom wanted to be picked up. Their daily delight at his appearance was something I occasionally resented; Mom the Boring Caretaker changed diapers, supervised naps and playtime, fed and cleaned everyone and everything, and when Daddy came home, he was the Hero, the Fun Parent. But they all looked so cute, Ken balancing one on each hip, Mike showing him a toy rocket and Sarah tugging on his hair. Graciously concluding the scene, he kissed them both on the forehead and set them down. "Daddy'll be back after he changes out of his work clothes."

"We're eating in five minutes, Daddy," I said, taking plates out of the cupboard. "How about a glass of wine to celebrate the family being back together?" When he didn't answer, I turned and realized he'd already gone up the stairs. The kids were looking up at me. "Okay, everyone wash hands. Let's go."

Mike led Sarah into the bathroom and I heard the water running. Ken came down in jeans and a sweatshirt, and at last we sat down. I listened to his account of his day, sort of dreading having to repeat everything I'd spent two hours telling Joanne, but when it was my turn to talk, I launched in, and got all excited again, going into the most minute detail;

all the while monitoring both kids to make sure they were eating and not fussing, not spilling anything, and answering their questions with a mother's infinite patience. I kept trying to picture Meg in that role. What if I gave her twins? Could she handle it?

After dinner I sent the kids back to the den. *I'll never use the TV set as a babysitter,* I'd earnestly promised Ken when I was pregnant with Mike. Now I wondered what I'd do without it. As he started to edge out of the kitchen, I said, "Did you read the application I filled out for IVF Canada? I made a copy of it and left it on your desk."

"No."

I waited for him to explain, and when he didn't, prompted, "How come?"

"I didn't get a chance. I will."

"It's sort of important to me."

"I know. I'm sorry."

"Want to read it now? I'll go get it."

"No. I can look at it later."

Look at it? What, walk by the desk and verify the existence of the stack of papers? Exhausted and feeling resentful, I said in a sullen voice, "You don't *have* to, if it's such a huge imposition."

His eyes met mine. "I didn't say it was a huge imposition."

"It sounded like it! Like you couldn't care less about what I'm going through!"

"Well it's not like I have much involvement in this."

"Are you serious? Your wife - the mother of your children - is going to carry someone else's child for the next nine months. You don't think you're involved in that?"

"It's your body, it's their baby. What do you want from me?" He held out his hands, palms up. "I'm here for you. That's all I can do."

"Just saying you're here for me doesn't mean you're supporting me emotionally!" My voice rose. "I'm about to disrupt our lives completely! It would be nice to know that's okay with you!"

In a perfect world, Ken would put his arms around me and whisper tenderly, "Shhh. I know. I'm sorry. You're right. I think what you're doing is amazing, I'm in awe of you. I'm so lucky to have such an incredible wife!" And then the fight would be over.

But it wasn't a perfect world, and he didn't do that, he stared me down, annoyed at my petulance, and left the room. I did the dishes, then put on a cheerful face and got the kids into bed, read them stories, and turned out the lights.

Is it Possible that a Six-Year Old has Better Insight Than Two Adults?

I like to sulk. A lot. And I like when the people who are responsible for my sulking know it. I lay next to Ken in stony silence; a dramatic departure from cheerful, chatty me. When he didn't say anything, I blew out a loud sigh.

"*Okay*," he said. "Let's talk about it."

"Talk about what?"

"About you being mad at me."

"Why should I be mad at you?"

"Because you think I should be more involved."

"Don't you think you should be?"

"I guess I just feel like we're not close enough yet for me to get all caught up in it. I'm sure once you're pregnant I'll feel more like it's really going to happen."

He had a point. Which I hated, I hated that he had a point.

"In my defense though," he went on, "I think about 80% of all husbands on the planet would have just said no to this. I've been thinking about the guys I work with, and I can't imagine any of them renting out their wives' bodies for nine months. For free."

I was so *not* going to get the apology I wanted! But maybe this was better, hearing his side. I rolled over to face him. To me, he still looked like the kid who used to hang out with Lisa. A few years older, they were just friends. During a trip home from the University of Miami, he stopped in to visit her and found me instead; sixteen and with breasts that I guess took him by surprise, because he was very attentive. That's a euphemism for "we made out on the couch."

In love with him again, I touched his cheek. "Thank you for telling me."

"I'll try to be more involved. It's still weird for me."

"For me too."

And with that, we forgave each other. Another euphemism.

"Mike's almost six, I want to tell him," I said to Ken the next morning. "He's old enough."

Ken, enjoying an unexpected bounty of eggs, hash browns and toast - my re-connection gesture - nodded. "Wait until I come home and we'll tell him together." His re-connection gesture. Finishing his coffee, he wiped his mouth with his napkin, and stood. "Thanks for such a great breakfast."

"My pleasure." We lingered over a kiss. "Maybe tonight you'll get dessert," I said.

"Mmm."

"MO-OM! Sarah won't get outa my room! I gotta get ready and she's staring at me!"

"Have fun at work," I said to Ken, kissed him again - this time a brief, distracted wife kiss - and hurried up the stairs to stop Sarah from staring at her brother.

"Hey, Bud. Talk to you for a second?"

Mike, occupied with his evening programs, looked up, curious at the serious tone of Ken's voice. He didn't object when I shut off the television. Sarah was singing to her stuffed bear and didn't even notice.

"Okay."

Ken and I sat on either side of him.

"It's about our friends Meg and Patrick," I began.

"What about 'em?"

"Well, Meg looks fine, but really, she's very sick. She takes a lot of pills every day to stay healthy."

"What's wrong with her?"

"She has Cystic Fibrosis."

Mike nodded. "I heard of that."

"You have?"

"Yeah, they talked about it on one of my science shows. But it's called *sixty-five roses*, Mom, not what you said."

Ken and I smiled. "Anyway," Ken went on, "because she's sick, Megan can't have a baby."

"Oh."

"So Mom is going to have the baby for her. Just like she had you and Sarah."

Sarah, hearing her name, stood and walked over, arms open in the universal *Pick me up!* posture of kids. I pulled her onto my lap. No reason why she couldn't be in on the discussion.

Mike, deep in thought, fiddled with the zipper on his sweat jacket. "How's the baby get inside Mom's stomach?" he asked after a minute. "Through her mouth?"

I glanced at Ken - his question or mine? He said nothing. Mine. "Well," I said, "they inject it... do you know what inject means?"

"Nope."

"Inject means to sort of... squirt in with a needle."

"They squirt the baby in?"

"The beginnings of a baby, when it's really tiny."

"Into your tummy? Or lower?"

"Lower."

"Well," he said, "I hope the doctor wears gloves, cause that could get messy."

"I'm sure he'll wear gloves." Only by not looking at grinning Ken did I manage to keep from laughing. "Actually, the messy part doesn't come until later."

"Whatcha mean?"

"Well after I deliver the baby, there's stuff left inside. Afterbirth. But it can't stay inside, it has to come out."

"How's it come out?"

I glanced at Ken - *a little help here?* - and he broke into a grin. "What Mom is trying to say is, we have to go to Toronto for this, which means we can go to the Hockey Hall of Fame!"

Mike's eyes got huge. "We can? Cool!"

I sat back, my one-of-a-kind story about bestowing the precious gift of life handily eclipsed by sports.

I got the kids to bed, and went downstairs to find Ken sitting at the kitchen table finishing off the coffee cake I'd baked earlier in the week - just eating it from the pan with his fingers - and washing it down with a scotch. "That went well," he said.

"I know." I sat down and grabbed a piece before it was completely gone, but shook my head when he offered his drink. "I think he knows all he needs to know. If he has questions, he can ask; otherwise, let's not bring it up."

"Agreed. We don't want it to become the focus of his life."

"Wasn't he so grown up about it!"

"Yeah, he was great. So now I guess I have to tell my folks."

"Good idea. You don't want them to find out from Mike. *Hey Grandma and Grandpa, didja know my mom is having someone else's baby injected down there?*

"Yeah, they'd love that." He smirked. "So I'll call them tomorrow."

"Okay." I didn't envy him; my in-laws were not the

most receptive people.

The phone rang just as I was headed out the door with Sarah to meet Joanne for lunch. I hesitated. Pick up or ignore? It rang again and I picked up.

"Laurie!"

"Eileen! How are things back in New Jersey?"

"Quiet since you left. Bern says he'll never replace you, the best paralegal he ever had."

"Oh go on," I laughed. "How's he doing?"

"Good! Busy with clients. Don't laugh, but he's got me doing something I always said I would never do..."

"No way... working?"

"Yes!"

"Doing what?"

"Paperwork, answering phones. Just until summer. So what's new with you and Ken? How are the kids?"

"We're all fine." I looked at my watch. I had maybe five minutes. Just enough time to tell her what I was planning to do, so I started in.

"Hold on, hold on," she interrupted right away. "Let me get Bern on the extension so he can hear this too."

He got on and I explained again about Meg. I expected them to be excited, but there were a few seconds of heavy silence.

"Really," said Bern finally.

"Yeah, it's the only way they can have a child."

"And they're compensating you for costs, but not paying you?"

"She said they're not paying her," Eileen said.

"She should have worked something out so she'd be

taken care of. She's letting them use her body for nine months. More, if you count recovery time."

"This is, like, her best friend. She can't charge her best friend."

"I'm right here," I reminded them.

"Sorry, Laurie," Eileen said. "We're just surprised."

"The other thing is, I don't want to see you hurt," added Bern.

"Hurt?"

"Disappointed. That it might not work out."

"Why won't it work out?" Eileen asked.

"I didn't say it wouldn't work out! I said *if*."

"If I can't get pregnant, Meg and I will still be friends," I assured him, a little annoyed.

"I know. But it's like I always told you. Be prepared for anything."

"Oh God," said Eileen. "The *be prepared for anything* advice."

"I'm prepared," I said.

"Also, financially, you should've..."

"Bern, stop telling her what to do!"

"Hey you guys, I'm meeting someone and I'm running late, and Sarah is fussing..." unfair, because she was sitting on the couch good as gold, waiting patiently, "and I need to go. Can we talk again sometime?"

"Are you okay, Laurie?" Eileen asked.

"I'm fine, just in a hurry."

"I'm sorry if Bern hurt your feelings."

"I didn't hurt her feelings. I just said..."

"I just really have to go. Take care, you guys!" I hung up, disappointed that they hadn't been more supportive. Maybe that was one of my faults, my tendency to have expectations of others. Something to tell the psychologist? *I have this habit of wanting people to be nice and caring and treat me with respect and decency, the way I would treat them.* The psychologist shakes his head. *That's a bad habit. People never react the way you expect them to.*

Ken came home that night, and I could tell from his expression that he'd told his parents. We had a pleasant dinner featuring Mike telling us what he'd done that day. He was at that chatty age where he didn't leave out a single detail, which could be tedious, but which I knew was a phase that would end even before he hit puberty.

"...and so my cloud was red and the teacher said how come the cloud is red and I said I saw a red cloud once and I really liked it and she said it was okay and then Billy said he saw a red cloud once, and guess what?"

"What?"

"He changed his cloud so it was red too!"

"My son the trend setter!" I said. "So where's the picture?"

"It's still at school, but we can bring them home next week and you can see it."

"Sounds like one for the fridge. Huh, Mom?" Ken asked.

"Sounds like it!"

After supper, I hustled the kids into the den with toys, and met Ken in the kitchen. "So tell me what they said."

He sat at the table. I poured him a scotch and sat across from him.

"Well, they have a few concerns. Some of which are legitimate. Some of which are just, well, my parents being who they are."

"Were they mad?"

"Furious!"

"Well at least you told them. I'm sure it came as a shock. They'll need some time to process it. I bet in a coupla days..."

"An hour."

"What?"

"An hour later my dad called back and left a voice mail saying something to the effect that he needed the name of the surrogacy lawyer, quote - as soon as possible - unquote."

"Why?

"He said he had some things to discuss with him."

"What kinda things?"

"Well, I called him back to ask. Turns out, they're concerned about the child's right to be an heir to their estate."

"What?"

"Yeah. God forbid they should ask how you're feeling, how Meg is feeling, when will the happy event take place." He finished his drink. "Give them those coupla days? They'll come through with a questionnaire to be filled out."

Of course I thought he was joking, but sure enough, they called the next day to ask a barrage of questions which I could tell they were reading from a list. First was what Ken had told me they wanted to know: *Will this child have the right to any monies from our estate?*

"No. The baby won't be mine or Ken's biologically."

"Seems very strange that she should ask you to carry her baby," said my mother-in-law. "If you're willing to go through childbirth again, you should have one of your own!"

"She didn't ask me. I offered. And Ken and I have already decided that we don't want more kids."

"Just like that you go and decide something so big!"

"Not *just like that*. We talked about it a long time. Even before we had Sarah, we said we only wanted two."

"It's just so *unnatural*, Laurie."

"Either way," interjected my father-in-law, "I intend to speak to the lawyer handling this."

The nerve! "I'm sorry, I don't think that's appropriate. I would rather you not call him."

"We need to know for sure that they won't have a right to our estate."

"I'm telling you for sure that they won't."

"You better be right about that!"

"Another thing," said my mother-in-law. "What happens if Patrick's business fails?"

"Why do you need to know about that?"

"Because who will pay the child's expenses if he's out of work?"

Like we were discussing a puppy. "Patrick's business is doing better than ever, and Meg's family is extremely well off. And even if they didn't have a lot of money, they'd find a way to feed their kid. It's what parents do."

"So you'll be under no obligation to send them money?"

"Of course not!"

"Can you catch Cystic Fibrosis from doing this and pass it down to Mike and Sarah?"

"Cystic Fibrosis is a genetic mutation that you're born with, you can't catch it."

"Good. Now, what about your own kids? Have you considered the effect this will have on them?"

Deep breath, deep breath. "When I was carrying Sarah, I made sure Mike was taken care of. While I carry this child, Mike and Sarah will continue to be my number one priority. I would never, in a million years, do something that would be bad for them! I resent your insinuation that I would!"

"The next question," began my mother-in-law, then

faltered.

But my father-in-law had no compunction about asking: "What will Ken do about his sexual needs while you are carrying this other couple's child?"

"What?"

"He's our son, we have a right to know."

"No you don't!"

"One last question," he went on, not at all rattled by my umbrage, "does Meg mind that her child is being carried by a Jew?"

My mouth dropped open and I couldn't answer.

"These are reasonable questions," my mother-in-law said.

"From now on, please direct all your *reasonable questions* to Ken." I snapped, and hung up.

Wearing an angry expression, Ken listened as I recounted the conversation.

"I'm going to call them! I'll make them apologize! There's no excuse for that!" He reached for the phone.

"No, don't bother." His outrage was gratifying and allowed me the opportunity to be grown up and understanding. "They are who they are, we can't change them."

"Are you sure? I'll call them right now."

"No, it's fine." I smiled.

Impressed, he hugged me. "You're incredible." Releasing me, he said, "Hey, you need to get away. Let's go to New Jersey this weekend. See your family. We can celebrate Mike's birthday a little early."

"Really?"

"Set it up, we'll do it."

Mike and Sarah slept most of the way and I found an oldies station that played a bunch of Ken's and my favorite songs. We sang along, laughing at how we remembered so many of the words.

When we arrived I was dismayed to see Rob looking thinner and more frail. But he had a nice surprise planned - he would help Mike bake his own birthday cake! "Any recipe you want," he said.

"Chocolate with chocolate frosting," Mike said right away, wiggling with excitement.

"If you're sure that's enough chocolate," Rob said, ushering him into the kitchen, with a wink at me. "No one bother us for a while, we're busy!"

As we drove away, Ken saw the tears in my eyes. He said nothing, because the kids were still awake, but reached over and took my hand.

"We'll be back again soon. Plus he promised to visit this summer."

"I know." I sniffed, wiped, sniffed again.

"He's doing fine."

"It's just hard, seeing him so weak. He always picks up the kids, and this time he didn't. Did you notice?"

"Yes."

I sighed and looked out the window. I hated that he'd noticed.

Help Me Prove I'm Sane

I lay awake, sick to my stomach, thinking that everything about Rob was fading, thinning, becoming small. Only his warm smile was the same. I could still remember how scared I was when he told me he was gay; how AIDS was my very first thought, how I wanted to grab his shoulders and shake him and make him promise to be careful, *so* careful! But after a while I'd convinced myself that he'd be spared because he was so sweet and generous, and in a committed relationship. Not the AIDS "type."

I forced my mind away from that and listened to Ken's breathing, envious, and tempted to wake him so I wouldn't be alone. But I knew there was nothing he could do or say that would make me feel better. I finally dropped off to sleep at around 2:00 A.M.

It seemed only a few seconds had passed when I woke up, sensing that someone was in the room. I opened my eyes, and to my astonishment, saw my friend Susan standing at the foot of my bed.

"Hey, Laur," she said as casually as if we were meeting for coffee.

I sat up, mouth hanging open. "Wha... what are you doing here?"

"I'm visiting from the Great Beyond, silly, whadya think I'm doing?"

"But... but you died five years ago!"

She grew serious. "I need to tell you something. It's really important. Can you be quiet and listen?"

What she used to say to me when she was alive. I

nodded.

"I want you to stop saying I died. You're still in the Earth Dimension so it's hard for you to grasp this, but souls don't die, we cross over. I want you to start saying 'cross over' instead of 'die.' Do you think you can do that?"

"But I..."

"Can you do that?"

I nodded. She smiled. "So many of the things you think are important aren't," she said, "and so many of the things you think aren't important *are*."

"Like what?"

"Like dancing, Laurie! Dancing is important!" She stood up, performed a single perfect pirouette, and was gone.

I was still sitting and staring when Ken mumbled, rolled over, and put his hand on my back.

"You okay?" he inquired sleepily.

I looked at the clock on his side of the bed. Three A.M. "I just spoke to Susan," I said.

Silence, then, "Your friend Susan?"

"Yes."

"The one who died?"

"She didn't die, she crossed over." Suddenly shivering with cold, I lay down, snuggled in his arms, so grateful for him. "Ken, we're awake right now, aren't we?"

"You are."

"But I mean... I *saw* her."

Unconvinced, he kissed the top of my head, and within seconds was asleep again. I lay awake the rest of the night thinking about what was important, what wasn't, and trying to remember the last time I had danced.

Nervously I sat in the office of Dr. Vickie Moore, the psychologist who would or wouldn't stamp the word SANE across my forehead. I checked my watch ten thousand times, wondering where Ken was; he was supposed to be present for the first meeting, and then Dr. Moore and I would meet a week later alone.

"We'll give him a few more minutes," she said pleasantly.

"Okay. I'm sure he'll be here soon." Was she watching me for signs that I was going to freak out? Determined to stay calm, I took in and let out a deep breath, checked my watch again, inspected my fingernails which were bitten right to the quick, tucked them in my lap, checked my watch again.

"Maybe we should begin," she suggested. "Does that sound okay?"

I nodded.

"Okay. So you want to be a surrogate."

I nodded again. Got scared she'd think I was an idiot for nodding twice, and added in a voice so formal it bordered on British, "Yes. I do. Very much so." *Okay, that's enough, shut up now.* "I want to do it very much."

She smiled. "There's no reason to be nervous."

"I'm not." *Liar!* "I am a little. I'm a little concerned about Ken." *Good word, concerned, so much better than worried, worried sounds so neurotic. And I'm not neurotic. Most wives would have freaked out, and look at me! So calm!* I checked my watch again. "He's usually so prompt."

"I'm sure he'll join us soon."

But he didn't, and the hour passed with her asking about my motives, what I hoped to achieve, was I having any negative feelings, how did my family react. She was shocked when I told her about Ken's parents, and shook her head, probably thinking that alone justified my going into therapy full time.

"Well okay, good," she said in a concluding kind of voice. "When you return next week you'll be taking the MMPI-2. It's a personality profile."

"Okay." We shook hands and as she escorted me to the door I said, "I'm sorry Ken didn't show up. I just can't imagine where he is."

"You did fine alone. See you next week."

I was going to kill him. If he was late or lost, he should have called. Was he dead? If he was dead I wouldn't kill him. After all that talk about how he was going to be more involved... !

His car was in the driveway, and as I pulled in, he stepped out onto the porch looking guilty and nervous.

"I got so lost!" he said before I could get a word out. He hurried down the steps. "I got so lost and couldn't find the place and I didn't have the number to call, and I just drove and drove! I'm so sorry, I know how important this was to you, and it was important to me, too! Please don't be mad."

I sighed about as hard as I have ever sighed in my life, because with him so sorry, I couldn't be mad, which meant I had to be okay, which I wasn't in the mood to be yet. "I gave you directions," I said.

"I know, but when it was time to leave, I couldn't remember where I put them. I thought I'd be able to find the place without them, but I couldn't. I kept asking people, and no one knew where it was. I was going crazy!" The more he talked, the more he wore me down, and he knew it, he could tell I was losing interest in being upset. Taking my hand, we headed up the steps together. "So tell me what I missed."

"She's really nice. And the more I talk about why I'm doing this, the better I feel."

"You should feel good, you're doing an amazing thing." When we went inside, Mike and Sarah flung themselves into my arms, so glad to see me, as if I'd been gone for days. I knelt and hugged them in a near rib-breaking embrace; felt *so* lucky.

Dr. Vickie Moore's Preliminary Comments:

When I asked Laurie Miller about her "positive expectations" with regards to the surrogacy plan, she referred to the fact that she can be instrumental in helping her friend Meg realize her dream of having a baby. Her "negative expectations" include morning sickness and other discomforts of pregnancy which she perceives as minor inconveniences. I asked how she imagines she will feel going through pregnancy and delivery with no baby to take home. Laurie stated that she will be ecstatic for Meg and anticipates some sense of loss and feelings of sadness: "but not to the point that I would want the baby." She feels that she did not bond immediately with her own children and does not, therefore, expect to have any major difficulties with respect to separating from her friend's baby. Laurie also noted that she and Meg had a great deal of contact within the last six months and she worries that, after this is over, they will go back to the "old relationship" with relatively infrequent contact; something, she said, which would be hurtful to her.

A week later I was back in Dr. Moore's office to take the test. To my surprise, she handed me a 75-page booklet. "Six hundred questions," she said apologetically.

"Wow." I hadn't expected so many. Taking a seat in a small cubicle outside her office, I was surprised by the nature of the questions:

Do you enjoy hurting small animals? No.
Do you faint at the sight of blood? No.
Are you fascinated with fire? No.
Are you frightened by crowds? Yes.
Have you ever used the hankie technique?

Okay, that one stumped me. A little timidly, I stepped into her office, tapped on the door.

She looked up with a warm smile. "Yes?"

"One of these, I can't answer." I held it out for her to see.

"Oh gee," she said. "The hankie technique is when you drop your handkerchief in order to get the attention of a man. I guess some of these questions are a little dated."

"A *little* dated?"

"A lot dated. Just keep going."

"They asked if you enjoy hurting small animals?" Ken asked, amused.

I nodded. "Yeah. I guess it's okay if I enjoy hurting big animals. But if I enjoy hurting small animals, it's a red flag. Then they started combining questions: Do I like setting fires? Have I ever set fire to a small animal?" We laughed. Easy, now that it was over. "I think that if I was going to hijack an innocent couple and force them to let me carry their baby, I'd keep quiet about my tendency to set animals on fire."

"*Small* animals," Ken clarified. "Big ones are okay."

Dr. Vickie Moore's Summary and Recommendations:

Laurie Miller is an intelligent, well-adjusted woman who is highly motivated to help her friend have a baby. Her motives are altruistic, based upon love and friendship; she would not consider being a surrogate for a stranger or for money. Since the baby will not be her genetic child, she is not likely to have great difficulty separating from the baby. And, of course, Laurie expects to have an ongoing relationship with parents and child, so the loss is not expected to be "final." Laurie is functioning well and has a happy marriage and a fulfilling life. Her personality assessment reveals a normal clinical profile, with no significant areas of difficulty. She is coping well with life stressors and problems, and is able to acknowledge areas of conflict. She and her husband Ken have a good relationship, communicate well, respect each other's autonomy and appear to be united in their approach to life's challenges. In light of the above, I see no reason why Laurie should not be permitted to proceed with the surrogacy plan as it was described to me. I recommend her without reservation.

"Let me get this straight, they said you're *not* crazy?" Joanne teased.

"All I had to do was act normal," I grinned. "Plus Patrick's results came back negative for the CF gene. We knew he didn't have it, but still, it's good to know for sure."

"One less thing to worry about! So what's next?"

"Dr. Moore sent a copy of the evaluation to IVF Canada, and I'll fly to Toronto on the 9th day of my cycle so they can test my LH level."

"What's that?"

"It tells them whether or not I'm ovulating. Meg is going to have another consult with a doctor at IVF because we're both getting really confused. She said she thinks my LH surge won't be timed with the retrieval of her eggs, that they'll be retrieved when they're ready, before they're released; meanwhile the doctor will monitor my LH surge to determine when my uterine lining is thick enough to receive the embryos."

"You know I have no idea what you just said, right?"

I sighed. "I have to trust that they know what they're doing. They sent me a pile of paperwork and it's so dense. I can't read it."

"Does Ken understand it all?"

"He might," I said, "if he bothered to look at any of it."

"Oh?"

She waited, granting me permission to vent. But I didn't feel like it. I had to stay focused on the fact that in the big picture, Ken supported the idea. It was like, he was willing to drive me to the mall but wasn't interested in going into any of the shops with me. I had to be happy with that.

"What's the matter, Laur? You sound funny," Meg said during that night's phone call.

I battled the impulse to say I was fine; lying would have been so much easier than being honest. "I'm down," I admitted.

"How come?"

"I don't know. I've been trying to figure it out."

"Maybe you're nervous?"

"Maybe."

"Laurie," she said, and I heard the fear in her voice, "are you going to back out?"

"Of course not! It's just, I guess I just feel guilty about putting people out. I keep having to dump the kids on Joanne, I keep having to ask Ken to take time off from work. You know me, I hate to inconvenience anyone. It's not a big deal, I'll work through it," I added swiftly, not wanting her to feel guilty. "I'm probably just being neurotic, obsessing about every little thing."

"You know if you ever need to talk, I'm here."

"I'll be fine."

"Okay. Hey, I spoke to Mitchell Galvin. He's drawing up the papers, which by the way you have to pick up and sign and mail to me before you come. Oh, and guess what?" Her tone turned impatient. "Patrick and I have to buy life insurance for you. We have to come up with an agreed-upon amount."

"Okay, I'll talk to Ken, since that's what he does for a living."

"Well Patrick and I decided that $100,000 would be okay."

"Oh," I said. "Well let me talk to Ken, okay?"

"Okay."

I hung up with her and called Ken.

"Are they serious?" he asked. "A hundred thousand? That's the price they put on your life? Do they realize that if, God forbid, something happened to you, that money has to take care of our two kids? You need to tell her it's not enough."

"What amount should I give?"

"Five hundred thousand, at least."

He sounded bitchy and serious, so I hung up with him and called her back.

"Five hundred thousand?"

"It's what will make us comfortable."

"That's a lot of money!"

"I know."

"Everything about this is so expensive, Laurie, you have no idea. The procedure, your trips back and forth, the phone bills... and now this."

"I'm sorry," I responded mechanically; what I wanted to say was, *At least you're not paying for surrogacy services, and the actual baby is free too!* "But the difference between the premium on $100,000 of life insurance and $500,000 is so small, and besides, you can cancel the policy as soon as I have the baby - you won't even have to carry it for the whole year."

"I'll talk to Patrick," she said grimly.

"Okay."

We hung up and more than anything in the world I wanted some time to cry, but Sarah tugged at my jeans and asked for a story.

"How about a nap?" I suggested. "Mommy will even nap with you. Won't that be fun?"

"No nap. Story."

I crouched and addressed her earnestly. "I know you find this hard to believe, Sarah, but one day you'll realize that a nap is the best thing in the whole wide world."

"*No nap.*"

"Okay, okay." I followed her into the living room. Hopefully later there'd be time to cry.

Two days later I got my period. I called Meg, all excited. "Remind me what I do now?"

"Be bloated and miserable for five days."

"Uh huh?"

"Then in nine days, come here to have your LH level tested. I have to call my doctor. If you got your period today, I have to start Lupren shots tomorrow."

"You have to go to the doctor every day for the shots?"

"No, Patrick will give them to me."

Impressed, I said, "I wouldn't let Ken with a hypodermic needle within ten miles of my butt."

"No offense to Ken, but neither would I. Okay, I have to call the doctor. Bye!"

"Bye." I hung up with her and called Ken. "I have to be in Toronto on June 9th."

"Who's going to watch the kids?"

"Joanne said she would. I hate to keep asking her. I'd take them with me, but that would be two extra tickets and we'd have to pay for those. So what I'll do is get Mike off to kindergarten, Sarah to Joanne's, and catch an early flight. Can I get a ride to the airport?"

"It's a weekday?"

"Yes."

"Well, even if you get an early flight, I won't get to work until noon."

I waited for him to say *but that's okay* and when he didn't, I said, "Are you kidding?"

"No, because If I take you in, drop you off, head back to the office..."

"No, I mean are you kidding? You might not take me?"

On his end, righteous indignation. "Oh, what, you're mad at me now?"

"Don't you dare turn this around!" I said. "All I'm asking for is a ride to the airport!"

"I can't keep taking time off work, Laur."

I was silent for a long time, then said in a stern, steady tone, "I'm asking you to do this for me. Please."

His turn to be silent; then he said, "Okay."

I felt bad when we hung up - bad about having to ask him, bad that he wanted to say no, bad that I made him agree. I knew to expect an occasional failure to see eye to eye. But I wasn't even pregnant yet!

"I'm growing follicles," Meg reported on the seventh day.

"Mazel Tov!"

"We'll probably have the transfer on the 12th or 13th. Can you believe we're getting this close?"

"So exciting! And Ken and I just got back from our appointment with Mitchell Galvin. We signed the Surrogacy Parenting Agreement."

"Hurray!"

I didn't mention that nowhere on the ten-page document was the life insurance amount specified, just that it would be bought for an agreed-upon amount. The primary function of the contract was to protect Meg and Patrick, but one clause did require that they buy me maternity clothes as needed. Again, no amount was specified. With Joanne as a witness, I signed.

"Laurie," said Meg, "when you get here you have to have some shots too. Progesterone and HCG."

"For what?"

"Progesterone to increase your chances of getting pregnant and staying pregnant. I think the HCG is for the same thing, but I'm not sure."

"How many of each do I need?"

"I don't know."

"Do I have to keep getting them after I come home?"

"I don't know. We'll ask when we talk to them."

"Meg, this pisses me off! Why am I just now finding this out? Does anyone know the long-term effects of those shots?"

"I don't know. We can ask."

"I mean, I'm sort of involved in this process! It would have been nice to know all this before now! Not that I wouldn't have agreed to it all, but..."

"I know, I'm sorry."

Her apology made me feel worse. "It's not your fault. I guess I'm just cranky."

"That's okay. Tell me when your flight gets in."

I gave her the details and we hung up. Then I added progesterone and HCG to my 20-item list of things to research at the library. Obviously if I didn't ask questions I wasn't going to get answers.

Retrieval and Implantation

When I got off the plane on the morning of June 9th and went through Customs, Meg was again waiting behind the glass. As always, the sight of her rekindled my excitement, and I hugged her so hard that she said let go, she couldn't breathe! Stepping back, I studied her.

"You look run down. Are you okay?"

She steered me toward the exit. "I have a confession to make."

"What is it?

"Those shots you have to get? I've been getting them all week and they're horrible. My bum is killing me, and I'm tired and nauseous and dizzy."

"Oh."

"I'm sorry. I could have told you before, but it wouldn't change anything, you knowing in advance. Right? It would just give you more time to dread it. So I thought I'd wait until you got here."

"Gee, thanks."

"Are you mad?"

"No. I guess I'm glad I didn't know."

"Good. So what did you find out about the shots?"

"The progesterone does what you said - facilitates implantation of the fetus."

"What about the HCG?"

"It's a growth hormone that the body produces naturally during pregnancy. So if I have it in my system, my body thinks I'm pregnant and starts producing it on its own. I think."

"Sounds logical. We can ask all these questions when we get there. I want to stop at the golf shop, it's on the way to the clinic, is that okay? I want to pick up a little something for Patrick for Father's Day."

"Okay."

In The Sports Spot she went straight to a display of men's golf shirts, and pulled out one that was lavender with navy and yellow stripes and white collar. "Do you like this?"

"Do you want me to like it?"

She chuckled, but then her eyes filled with big tears that spilled down her cheeks.

"Hey!" I said, startled, "what's wrong?"

"I don't know. Maybe it's the hormones."

"Maybe it's the shirt." I took it from her and put it back. "Looking at it makes me want to cry too."

"Very funny." She wiped her eyes, and bought him a card and baseball cap instead. From there we went to the clinic and I got my first shot.

"Not so bad," I said as I rejoined her in the waiting room.

"That's exactly what I said a few days ago," she smirked. "Hey, guess what I just found out? I have to get one more shot."

"When?"

"Tonight at 10:30."

"Now that," I said, "is a pain in the ass." It was my last joke for 24 hours.

The next morning Meg had an ultrasound, while I got another progesterone shot, then a nurse who looked like she was 12 drew about half my blood, filling vial after vial.

"What are you going to do with it all?" I finally asked.

"The clinic needs maternal serum," she said.

"Which is...?"

"Maternal serum is, like, blood from the mother."

"Why didn't you say *that?*" Sitting there, my recently-poked cheek started to throb. "Obviously they need it. But for what?"

"They'll incubate the fertilized eggs in it, so they can, like, get used to being in your blood. Otherwise they get confused."

I pictured a dozen embryos carrying tiny suitcases getting into an elevator; the one nearest the panel looks for the button for the 20th floor, and as the doors close, they all realize at the same time that the buttons only go up to 19, and embryonic panic, a sort of metallic sounding high-pitched squeal, ensues. The *open door* button fails to function properly.

Suddenly dizzy; I wondered if she'd misunderstood directions and had taken too much blood.

"Are you okay? You look funny," she said.

"I'm fine." I returned to the waiting room, feeling hot and nauseous. Meg joined me, looking as bad as I did, and for the rest of the day, every hour, every moment, was consumed with some unpleasant task: checking in at a desk, getting a shot, feeling like crap, checking in at another desk, getting another shot, feeling like more crap. In silence we allowed ourselves to be processed like subjects in a bizarre research project. I was too sick to ask any questions, I just did whatever I was told. By the time we got home, I skipped dinner, just fell into bed, head spinning.

The next morning the phone woke me. I got up, felt okay; showered, dressed, and went into the kitchen.

"The clinic called," Meg said. "My levels have gone from 4580 to 8800."

"Up is good, right?"

"Up is very good! It takes 1000 to make one mature egg."

"A thousand what?"

"No idea. But it means I have eight mature eggs. I did it, Laurie! Oh my God, I made eggs!"

"Just coffee for me," I joked. We laughed, then both started to cry, this time tears of relief, excitement, and surprise.

"But enough about you," I said, "what are my levels?"

"Six hundred, which means you'll be 1000 today or tomorrow. I go in at 9:00 tomorrow morning and they'll retrieve my eggs."

I sat at the table. "Can you believe this? Seriously? Can you believe we're finally at this point?"

"I know!" She sat too. "I haven't even called Patrick yet, I wanted you to be the first to know."

"Call him! Right now!"

"Okay!" She picked up the phone and dialed.

I poured coffee and drank it cautiously. Stomach was more settled, but not great. I listened in on her conversation with Patrick, taking pleasure in her joy, trying not to focus on another day of shots and blood tests.

I managed to get down a buttered English muffin and another cup of coffee while she gave herself a breathing treatment, then we headed back to the clinic for another round. I fell asleep in the car on the ride home, something I hadn't done since I was about six, and Patrick practically had to carry me into the house. I called Ken to update him, see how the kids were, and fell right to sleep.

I woke at 6:00 to the sound of Meg pounding her chest, her morning routine. I waited it out, then went into the kitchen when I heard her making coffee.

"Today's the day!" I said, hugging her. "How do you feel?"

"Nervous. Not about the procedure, but the eggs. What if they don't..."

"Stop. They're fine."

"Laurie's right," Patrick announced, appearing in the doorway. He accepted the cup of coffee she handed him. "This is going to work. I just know it."

We nodded at her. She took a deep breath. "Yes. Okay."

"Rah rah team embryo!" I said. "I'll take a quick shower then we'll go."

Patrick poked his head into the waiting room where I was busy biting my nails. "She's fine! They got thirteen eggs. Twelve look good, one's a little iffy."

"Can I see her?"

"Yeah, she's in recovery. Come on."

I followed him down the hall into Meg's room. She was groggy and pale, but smiled when she saw me. "Hi!"

"A baker's dozen, Meg!" I said hugging her gently.

"Now we'll see if they fertilize."

"In my sperm? Trust me, they'll fertilize," Patrick bragged.

"The moment he's been waiting for," Meg said and we laughed. In that moment it hit me very hard: *We're going to make a baby!*

While Meg rested, I had a vaginal ultrasound, an oddly invasive experience that wasn't fun, exactly, but not altogether bad either. Then I checked in for my daily shot.

"This is clearly wrong," I told the nurse. "I'm here for a pedicure and scalp massage."

"Please hold still, Mrs. Miller."

Afterwards, as I sat battling nausea, Dr. Lee came in with good news. "Your endometrium is almost thick enough to receive the embryos!"

"Me and my big fat endometrium," I said as enthusiastically as I could without puking.

"So we'll be implanting them as soon as they're ready."

Again, the visual of embryos with suitcases; this time in an airport staring up at the monitors - *Departure from petri dish: today. Arrival to Laurie's womb: tomorrow.* "So I could be pregnant soon," I said.

"If all goes well."

If all goes well, I thought as he left. For the first time I felt nervous. What if something went wrong with me? The apprehension surrounding Meg was over; she'd done her part. Now it was up to me. What if the embryos didn't attach? What if they hated living in me and let go? What if... what if... what if...

As if from a great distance, Meg's voice: "Poor thing, she's exhausted," and then Patrick's: "Let's get her home."

I forced my eyes to open, saw them standing there, regarding me sympathetically. "Thick endometrium," I said, so tired the words were slurred.

Patrick helped me up. "Yes," he said. "You did great."

I called Joanne and filled her in. "Tomorrow is more shots for me and we wait for the eggs to fertilize in Patrick's sperm. Then they implant them and I get to come home."

"You're done with the shots?"

"No, I have to have HCG every four days and progesterone every two. I think. I don't know. I'm so tired and sick and sore, I can't even think straight."

"You sound horrible."

"Thanks."

"Ask Dr. Stoller if I can give you the shots. That way you won't have to keep going back."

"I'd love it; thanks, Joanne."

"We miss you. Sarah especially, but she's okay, don't worry, just get pregnant and come home!"

Patrick took another day off in order to drive us back to the clinic the next day. Meg was still sore from her procedure, and my demeanor was sluggish and vegetable-like. I endured more shots, and we went home in the middle of the afternoon. I napped and we were able to have a decent supper that night.

The next day the clinic called to say that Meg's eggs had reached the eight cell stage. And at 2:10 P.M., two embryos were injected through my cervix into my uterus. It was an easy process, and afterwards I lay slightly inverted, just the way Dr. Lee said I would. With eyes shut, I pictured the pair of embryos in their new pink home, unpacking their little suitcases.

At last settled in my seat on the plane headed back to Rhode Island, I read the note Meg had handed me as she dropped me at the airport:

June 14, 1994
Dear Laurie,

Wow! We're off! What a week! In some ways it feels almost like a dream. But then I return to reality when I see your face and it sinks in, the major endeavor that you have undertaken for Patrick and I. You are an incredible person and I was blessed 20 years ago when I met you on the swim docks!

This has been a very trying time for you, but I want you to know whether we are successful or not, this has shown me so much about myself that I really needed to know. Thank you, Laur, for doing that for me.

This is incredibly exciting. But at the same time, Patrick and I are keeping our excitement at bay because we are concerned about the pressure you may feel. Please don't. What will be, will be.

Thank you from the bottom of our hearts and beyond.
I love you,
Meg

Joanne's hand wavered a little as she gripped the syringe and prepared to jam the needle into my flesh. "What if I hit a major artery and you bleed to death?"

"I don't think there are any major arteries in the ass. Just do it, it'll be fine."

"You're absolutely sure you can't do it by yourself?"

"Absolutely completely sure. Just do it. You'll be fine."

I felt the jab, felt her withdraw the needle, then felt her press the alcohol pad against the site. "This part I can handle," I said, reaching around to hold it in place for a few seconds. "Thanks."

"Did it hurt?"

"Of course it hurt." I zipped up my jeans and faced her. "But it's supposed to. Honest, you were great, you were Florence Nightingale." I started to sit, thought better of it, and leaned. "So one week of this, then I go get my levels checked."

"What should they be?"

"Dr. Lee said that after a week anything over ten is good. And if it continues to go up by 70% a day, that'll be a good sign that I'm pregnant."

"But not for sure?"

"I don't know. I think if it's high then we do more tests or something. To confirm. I'm a bundle of nerves."

"Why?"

"Because what if this doesn't work? I'll have to be the one to tell her. How will she be able to deal with it?"

"That sounds like a really good thing *not* to think about right now," Joanne said sternly. "Just focus on everything working out."

"I will. Hey, thanks again, Joanne. I couldn't have done this without your help. How am I going to pay you back?"

"Oh stop. That's like Meg asking how she can pay you back." She hugged me. "Call me tonight."

"Okay."

After she left I checked to make sure Sarah was still napping, then lay down to wait out the nausea. I pictured the embryos still making the decision about whether or not to stay, discussing the pros and cons, when all of a sudden the warm, comforting progesterone fills their apartment, and they say, *It's pretty nice here. Let's give it a chance.*

I called Meg a week later. "Ninety-six!"

"Wow! That's high!"

"Dr. Stoller said that the number should be around 270 on Wednesday, and then we can really celebrate! And you know what, Meg? I *feel* pregnant. I can't explain it. I just do."

"I don't want to get my hopes up, so let's wait until Wednesday to see for sure."

"Okay, I'll call you!"

During the next two days I took on projects to keep myself busy - cleaned the basement, cleared out closets and cupboards. Told Sarah and Mike that I'd take them to the park, but was so preoccupied that I drove to the library instead, then sat blinking in confusion when Mike said, "Why are we *here*?" and Sarah, planning on swings and slides, not books, started to wail, "Mo-meeee! Nooo!"

At dinner Ken talked about his job. I half listened to him complain about clients who constantly called with questions and wasted his time, but couldn't commit to signing the paperwork. He didn't say a word about the impending pregnancy and neither did I. I was so scared I wasn't pregnant, and I think he was scared that I was.

Finally it was Wednesday, and Dr. Stoller called at noon. After I hung up with him, I called Meg. "We did it! We did it! My HCG is 360!"

"That's even higher than it has to be!"

"I know! I'm extra pregnant!"

"Oh Laurie!"

"I have to have a series of pregnancy tests, and my next appointment with him is the 19th. That's when we'll be absolutely sure. Even though I'm absolutely sure now."

"I just can't believe it! I can't get over it! I have to call Patrick!"

"Will you tell your dad?"

Silence on her end. Then she said, "I think I'll wait until we're sure."

"Okay." My heart broke. Why the secrecy? Why keep this joy from him when he had nothing but his disease to think about? I'd spoken to Rob everyday that week and we'd already compiled a list of ridiculous names for the baby: Cedrick, Jonas, Zeus..." Call Patrick," I said. "We'll talk in a few days."

On June 29th Dr. Stoller called me with my test results, and I called Meg. "It's for sure," was all I said.

She was silent for a minute, and then I heard her crying.

"Knock it off!" I started crying too. "We have too much to do! We have to think about baby clothes!" Tears changed to laughter. "Let's call our husbands," I said, "and make them take us out to dinner tonight."

"Yes! Good idea! Oh Laurie! Can you believe it?"

"Now I can!"

Unhappy Birthday

Bad cramps woke me in the morning. Wincing, I rolled over to tell Ken, but he wasn't in bed. The clock said it was almost ten. How had I slept so late? Pain surged hard, retreated. Frightened, I managed to grab the phone, and called Joanne.

"How bad are they?" she asked. "Scale of one to ten."

"Sixteen and a half. What should I do?"

"Do they feel like anything you've had before?"

"I'm not sure."

"What did you eat last night?"

"Chinese food. You think it's that?"

"Could be. Everyone else feels fine?"

"Yeah, I hear them out playing in the yard."

"Want me to come over?"

"No, I just want to lie here. Maybe they'll go away."

"Good. Maybe it was the food."

"I hope so." Cautiously, I sat up. Felt better. "I think I'll shower."

"Are you sure? I can run out and tell Ken if he's in the yard."

"I think I'm fine. I'll call you in a little while." A cramp prodded, not nearly as bad as before. "I think I'm fine," I said again.

"Probably the food. Go shower. I'm going to tell Ken to check on you."

"Thanks so much," I said. "Hey, want to have a pre-4th of July barbeque tonight?"

"I never need an excuse to have a barbeque," she

laughed. "I love that you're thinking about food."

I laughed too; told her I'd call her later. I swung my feet over the bed. Stood. Fine. Went into the bathroom and checked - no blood. *Thank God!* Halfway through my shower I heard Ken come into the bathroom.

"You okay?" he asked.

I poked my face out of the curtain. "I'm good except that I didn't get my morning kiss."

He stepped over and kissed me. "That's probably why you were crampy."

I closed the curtain and resumed my shower, smiling now. "I'm sure of it."

"Seriously, you feel okay?"

"I'm fine. Hey, Ken?" I poked my face out again. "Barbeque with Joanne and John tonight?"

"Sounds good. Want me to hang around until you get out?"

"No, that's okay. Go out and play with the kids."

"How are you?" John greeted me with a hug, unusual for him.

"I'm good," I said, surprised.

"I just wanted to say that I think what you're doing is great. Joanne told me what happened this morning, and I have to say, it sort of scared me. I would hate for anything to happen to you."

I was touched. "Nothing's going to happen to me."

But as the evening wore on, I began to feel uneasy, like on the verge of more cramps. I collected some dishes and shot Joanne a look that said *Come with me.* And as I went into the kitchen she was right behind me.

"You okay?"

"I don't know. Something's not right."

"What do you mean?"

"This doesn't feel like my other pregnancies."

"Well maybe some pregnancies feel different from other pregnancies."

"Maybe."

"You look tired. Let me get my troop home so you can go to bed. Okay? Don't do any dishes, I'll come over and do them tomorrow."

"Okay." Instead of going out to say goodnight to everyone, I went up to bed. Cried, ached, was anxious and miserable. Ken came up after everyone left, but I told him I was fine. I wanted to be alone, I didn't have the energy to try to define what I was feeling.

The next day I went to Dr. Stoller's office for blood work. Sitting in the waiting room, I had most of the conversation with Meg worked out in my head: *I'm so sorry Meg, something went wrong, but we'll try again, we've come too far not to!* when he appeared.

"We're up to 2224!"

My eyes opened wide. "Are you sure?"

He grinned. "I'm sure!"

"But you were only expecting 1200! Does this mean twins?"

"Let's not speculate yet. We'll just keep an eye on things."

I stood and hugged him. "Thank you so much! I can't wait to tell Meg!"

"Twins?"

"He didn't say twins, I did. He just said everything is fine and let's wait and see. I think he was thinking it, though."

"Wow!"

"Meg, I had some spotting on the way home, but I'm

not going to worry about it. I'm sure it's nothing. If it was bad, the numbers wouldn't be so nice and high."

"Okay. I'll give Dr. Lee a call and update him."

"Good idea. Hey, I'm going to do a few things, then lie down. Talk later?"

"Okay. Thanks, Laur!"

The cramps came back late in the afternoon, this time so bad that I couldn't stand up to make dinner. Ken had pizza delivered, and assumed responsibility for most of the conversation at the table so the kids wouldn't know anything was wrong. I spent the meal smiling and trying to eat. Right after, I went up to bed, hoping to feel better.

By 8:00 I was in such agony that I didn't even have the strength to call Ken's name; I lay doubled over in pain, praying he'd come in and check on me. Finally I crawled out of bed to the top of the stairs. "Ken?" I said in a feeble voice.

Mike's frightened face appeared at the foot of the stairs. "Dad!" he shouted, "something's wrong with Mom!"

Ken was at my side in a second; pressed his palm against my forehead then grabbed the phone: "Joanne, Laurie's in a lot of pain, please come over right away!" Sensing the tension, Sarah started to wail, while Mike's eyes, full of panic, met mine. I couldn't even smile to reassure him, all I could do was try to keep from screaming out; it was absolutely the worst pain I'd ever had, worse than kidney stones, a ruptured appendix, and two births, all put together.

Within a minute Joanne arrived. Scooping up the still-screaming Sarah, she said, "Everything's going to be fine, Mommy just has a belly ache." To Ken she said, "Did you call Dr. Stoller?"

"No, can you?"

"I'll do it right now." She took Mike's hand and reluctantly he followed her down the stairs.

With the kids gone I gave into the agony - groaning and gripping my stomach and crying. Ken kept trying to hold me, and I think he was almost in tears too. I heard Joanne's voice, "Dr. Stoller said to go to the ER. I'm going to call an ambulance."

Terrified, I clung to Ken. "I don't want to go to the hospital!"

"Let me get your robe and slippers. I'm going to grab some clothes in case you have to stay." He eased himself out of my grip, and started grabbing stuff. In a daze, I watched. And waited.

"How's the pain now?" asked the ER nurse.

"Naturally it's gone," I said. "Like it was never even there." I slid off the gurney. "So bye bye!"

"Not so fast," she chuckled. "We need to do an ultrasound."

"Okay." I didn't want her to. I wanted to believe the cramps were gone for good and the baby was fine. But I lay back and she ran the transducer over my belly. "Do you see the baby?"

"Well, no, but it's pretty early. I wouldn't automatically expect to see anything this soon." She moved it back and forth, back and forth. "It could be an ovarian cyst from the HCG shots."

"Those shots can cause ovarian cysts?"

"Yeah, it's a side effect."

"Would have been nice to know that up front!" I

fumed. But there was no one there to be angry with, and it wouldn't have stopped me anyway.

Ken took me home and gave Joanne a quick version of what happened while I went upstairs to check on the kids. Sarah was asleep, but Mike was awake, and as I leaned over him, his little arms were around my neck in a second, and he clung tight.

"Mom, are you okay?"

"Yes, it's just what Joanne said - I had a belly ache. But it's gone now. Can you sleep?"

He nodded, but didn't let go for a few minutes. And I didn't make him.

"We're going to stop the HCG," Dr. Stoller announced.

"And the progesterone?" I asked hopefully.

"No, we need to keep that up. Personally, Laurie, I'm not convinced it does any good. But IVF is adamant that we continue."

"The whole thing with them is getting so complicated," I said. "Two weeks ago they wanted me to schedule an ultra sound for the 14th, but then they called and said to reschedule for later, because nothing will show up that early. Which is just what the ER nurse told me when she did one."

"Right. To be honest, it's a little frustrating for me, too. Your HCG has continued to rise and I think the numbers are good, but IVF says they're borderline."

"Borderline?"

"I say let's keep that appointment on the 14th. See what's what. Okay? Then we'll really know where we stand."

"Okay, that sounds good."

The cramps kept coming back, not as bad as before, but with spotting. Dr. Stoller said it might indicate that one of the embryos didn't take. My HCG level was still rising, but not as much. Which made sense to me, if we were only dealing with one embryo now. But I wasn't the one with the medical degree. All I could do was assume everyone knew what they were talking about, and that my body would soon swing into normal pregnancy mode, the way it had twice before.

"Okay, I'm a little concerned," Dr. Stoller admitted the day of my ultra sound. "Your level was holding, but at this point I would consider it borderline."

I felt sick and desperate, like an earthquake was about to strike and ruin the city and there was nothing I could do about it.

"Let's see what the ultrasound shows," he said, "and then we'll talk. Until then, deep breaths and try to relax. Okay?"

I nodded. "Okay."

The tech took a long time with the ultrasound and kept murmuring, "Just a moment please," every time I asked what she saw. When she said, "I'll be right back," I knew we were in trouble.

For several minutes I lay on the table, cold, scared, and alone.

"Laurie?"

I propped myself up. "Hi, Dr. Stoller."

He took my hand. "Laurie, I have some bad news. You have an ectopic pregnancy. It's very dangerous. We have to perform immediate surgery."

"What? No!"

"I'm so sorry. Call Ken, and then you have to get prepped. You're going to be fine, I promise."

"So... there's no baby?"

"Not this time."

I lay back. Shut my eyes and tears rolled down the sides of my face. "Dr. Stoller?"

"Yes, Laurie?"

"Will you call Meg for me? I can't do it."

July 14, 1994, Transvaginal and transabdominal sonography were performed.

RESULTS:

The uterus is not enlarged. It is anteverted. It measures 11.3 cm in length from cervix to fundus by 5.4 cm AP by 6.6 cm transverse. Endometrium is 18 mm thickness. There is no intrauterine gestational sac present.

Right ovary measures 4.4 cm x 3.2 cm x 2.9 cm and contains a small to moderate sized cyst 2.0 cm in diameter and the inner walls are a little irregular but it is probably a small hemorrhagic cyst.

There is a mass in the left pelvis. It is moderately large. It is complex in appearance. It measures 5.6 cm x 3.8 cm x 4.6 cm. There are solid and Cystic elements within it and the whole complex suggests pelvic ectopic pregnancy, although a complex cyst of the left ovary itself might also cause this appearance and we were actually unable to definitely identify the left ovary.

CONCLUSION:
The uterus is empty.

I spent the next day, which happened to be my 35th birthday, in bed. Hormones raging through me made me feel like my whole life was a disaster - from losing Meg's baby to having ruined the birthday luncheon Joanne had planned for me. Sarah was at the top her game, running from room to room, shouting, "*Mommy! Guess where I am now!*" Ken, who had taken a few days off, did his best to keep her and Mike occupied, but it was starting to get to him. When the phone rang, I heard him answer with forced cheer. A moment later he appeared at my bed, picked up the extension, and handed it to me.

"Hello?"

"Laurie?"

"Oh Meg!" I started crying. "I'm so sorry!"

"Don't apologize! How are you feeling?"

"Still a little out of it. Shaky. Not eating much, if you can believe it," I tried to laugh.

"But you're fine now?"

"Yeah. The good news is, they tied my tubes. That means no more birth control!" When she didn't answer I thought how terrible that must have sounded to her, and went back to crying, "I'm so sorry I didn't call you."

"Don't be silly! Dr. Stoller was really nice about it. I understand why you didn't call, please don't worry about that."

"I was so scared. They took me in even before Ken got there!"

"Oh no!"

"I wanted them to wait, but who was I? Just the patient."

"I'm so sorry you had to go through it alone."

"Are you coming down, Meg?"

"Oh, Laurie, I can't. It's such a busy time for Patrick, and you know how hard it is for me to travel, it takes me a long time to prepare for it."

I was so sure that she was going to say she'd be on the next plane out that her words didn't even register for a few seconds. Then I said, "You're not coming?"

"I'm so sorry!" she said again. "I would if I could! You know that, right?"

"You can," I said. "You can get on a plane and come here and grieve with me! Meg, I'm a mess! I have never felt so horrible, so miserable, in my whole life! I need you here!" I couldn't believe I was actually saying what was on my mind; normally I would have just gone along with whatever she wanted to do. But blame it on the anesthesia. I heard sputtering on her end, sort of a helpless don't-know-what-to-do sound. I sighed. "Meg, I love you, but I'm really sad, and I know you have to be sad too. You just *have* to be. We both lost something precious, and I think we'll begin to heal better if we can spend some time together."

"Okay, Laurie. I'll work on making arrangements."

"Thanks. I need to sleep now, I'm really exhausted. Call me later, will you?"

"Okay. You rest up."

"Wait... Meg?"

"Yes?"

"I'm sorry."

"Just get better. I'll talk to you later."

Mortality

Physically, I recovered from the ectopic pregnancy right away. But the depression that followed was deep and unshakable. Raging hormones, guilt, the sense of loss, and sadness at not being able to share the experience with Meg, who kept saying she was having trouble setting up a visit, prevented me from healing emotionally. The worst part was forcing myself to be perky and attentive for Mike and Sarah. Many days I would have loved more than anything to stay in bed. But each morning I was up early, fixing breakfast for the family, kissing Ken goodbye, and keeping Mike and Sarah busy for the next 14 hours. Only Joanne knew the truth, and she frequently took the kids for a few hours while I napped or just sat and cried.

"No reason you can't try again," Dr. Stoller told me. In Toronto, Dr. Lee told Meg the same thing. But so far, she and I hadn't talked about it. I think she was afraid to bring it up. And I wasn't ready to commit to a decision yet. I wanted to want to try again. But that's not the same thing as wanting to try again.

Sometimes I'd be brushing Sarah's hair - so unbelievably silky soft the way only a child's hair can be - and I'd think *of course I'd do whatever it takes to give Megan one of these*. Other times I was scared out of my wits. What if I had died on the operating table? The thought of my kids without a mother made me feel sick to my stomach. What had I been thinking, risking their security? Never again! For weeks my heart was a battlefield as the two sides waged war.

Any other husband would have said *we're not going*

through that again! But calm, patient Ken said he would support me no matter what. It was his comforting presence that pulled me through, and by the time Meg finally arrived in August, I was almost back to my old self.

Dangling our legs in the pool we laughed at Sarah's attempt to do the same; short and stubby, hers hung over the side but didn't touch water. She finally got frustrated and demanded I take her in. So to the shallow end we went, my hands around her while she fake swam. I was aware of Meg's expression, and knew what she was thinking. Still, we kept the conversation general - husbands, fashion, movies. When I inquired about her father she said he was going downhill rapidly.

"Thank God I didn't tell him," she said.

I still thought that if she'd given him something exciting to think about he'd be better, but there was no point in mentioning it again. Holding Sarah tight, I went in circles. "You're *such* a good swimmer, Sarah!"

"How is Rob?"

I sighed. "Not good. We keep making plans for him to visit, but he's been so tired and sick. In bed a lot."

"I'm so sorry. Are there stronger medications he can try?"

"A few. He always does well when they switch him over to a new one." I carried Sarah out of the pool, wrapped her in a towel, and dried her off; covering her face and making her giggle. "How are you," I finally asked, "after what happened?"

"Well, disappointed, of course."

I waited for her to elaborate, then, when she didn't, said, "Did you and Patrick talk much?"

"Not really. We sort of just went on with our lives. Nothing you can do about it now, right? I mean, not to sound cold or anything but maybe we didn't expect instant success the way you did. We're not exactly the most optimistic people on the planet, I guess," she laughed.

I released Sarah, laid my towel next to Meg, and sat down, suddenly sorry for her. So unfeeling, so out of touch with her emotions! Was she afraid to be sad? Or was she the smart one? We passed the rest of her visit not talking about what happened, and three days later I dropped her off at the airport.

"Mom and Lisa and I think you should try again," announced Rob, stretched out on the deck chair beneath a blanket even though I was sweating in the late summer sun.

"Really?"

"Definitely."

"Why?"

"Because you can!"

He and Lisa and I laughed, thinking about that old joke, *Why does a dog lick his balls? Because he can.* My mother probably didn't know the joke, but she laughed too.

"Plus," said Rob, "it's a positive thing, and we all need positive." He paused, smiled wryly. "Well, the other kind of positive."

We laughed again, but this time it was forced, and Rob knew it. He sat up, regarding me seriously. "Know what I think, Laur?"

Convinced he was going to say something profound, I said, "What?"

"I think your violas would look better planted in clumps in your garden, not popping up between the bricks."

"Oh." I looked around the patio. It was true, they looked spindly and were constantly at risk of getting stepped on.

He pulled off the blanket and got up. "I can do it."

"Robert, no," my mother said.

But he went over and gently pulled out a fragile patch of the little purple flowers, roots and all, and replanted it along the edge of the brick lining the garden wall. "See?"

"Yes," I said. In a moment, Lisa and I were beside him helping. One by one, we moved all the viola plants, and when we were done, I took a picture - not of them but of him. "They look beautiful," I said.

But he knew. With a half smile, he teased, "You're just taking my picture because you think I won't be here much longer."

That time no one even pretended to laugh. Later, heading out of the kitchen, I passed him going toward the stairs.

"I have to lie down," he said. I saw exhaustion all over him - in his eyes, his shoulders, his walk, every move he made.

"Rob," I said suddenly, "If you're tired, you can stop."

"I did stop. I'm going to lie down."

"No, I mean... " I took a deep, shaky breath. "If you're doing this for us, you need to know that it's okay if you want to stop. It's okay if you need to let go." Tears spilled out of my eyes and rolled down my cheeks. "We'll miss you terribly, but you'll always live... in our hearts... we'll be okay..."

I broke down, sobbing. He put his arms around me and I held him tight, wondering how much time he had left. I felt him trembling and wanted to ask if he was scared, but didn't dare, for fear the answer would be yes.

Rob replanting the violas.

Ken's parents were next to visit. Five days of not talking about the surrogacy or the disastrous way it ended. I was never so glad to see a summer week end. But my relief was cut short by an emergency phone call from my mother on August 25th.

"Robert is in the hospital. He has pneumocystis pneumonia."

"Is he okay?"

"He has an oxygen mask on and *should* be resting!" I heard the affectionate note in her voice, and could picture her looking at him tenderly. "But he's going crazy reaching for the phone. I think he wants to talk to you."

"Put him on!" I said. I heard the phone being handed over, and said "Rob?"

"Laurie, did you decide yet?"

"Decide what?" I honestly had no idea what he was talking about.

"If you're going to try to get pregnant again."

"Oh Rob. I can't even think about that. I'd rather talk about you."

"Okay, let's talk about me. And what I want. Which is to hear that you're going to try again."

"You are such a nag!"

"It's one of the reasons you love me so much." His laugh turned immediately to a cough, then a choking, gasping sound that sent terror through me. I heard my mother's voice: *"Put your mask back on!"* and then Lisa picked up the phone.

"Don't panic," she said, "he's okay. Just short of breath."

"Should I come down?"

"No. They're giving him antibiotics and breathing

treatments. I'm sure he'll be better in the morning."

"Hug him for me," I said, trying not to think what I was thinking.

A few minutes before 7:30, the phone rang. I answered, and with a big smile, handed the phone to Mike. "For you," I said.

"Hello?" I watched his face light up. "Uncle Rob!"

Crouching, I listened in on the conversation.

"How ya doin, buddy?"

"Good! I'm starting first grade today and I stay the whole day!"

"I know, it's huge! That's why I called! You wearing your Yankees cap?"

"Uh huh!"

"Good man."

"Uncle Rob, are you still in the hospital?"

"Yeah, a few more days."

"Okay, um, I have to go now, maybe the bus is here."

"Okay. Don't forget to do all your homework! And pay attention to everything your teachers say."

"Okay, and you pay attention to what the doctors say!" Without saying goodbye, Mike handed me the phone and ran to look out the front door.

"You made his day," I said. "Thanks."

"I wasn't going to let it go by. Remember starting first grade?"

"No."

"Really? I do. Like yesterday."

"Well you're two years younger. Maybe when you're my age your memory won't be as good," I laughed; then was horrified - he wasn't going to ever be my age.

"Mom!" said Mike, "Bus is here!"

"I have to walk Mike out, can I call you back?" I asked urgently.

"No, I think I'll rest a little. We can talk later."

"Okay." How to repair the damage I'd just done? "Rob, I love you."

"I love you too, Laur." As if reading my mind, he added, "Don't worry about what you said."

"*Mo-om!*"

"I'm so sorry, I just wasn't thinking!"

"It's okay. Hey, I'm going to call Lisa. She's the *nice* sister." He let out a laugh and hung up. I felt myself smile as I walked Mike out to the bus.

The next call wasn't so cheerful.

"Laurie, it's Meg. My dad died last night."

"Oh, I'm so sorry!" It was on the tip of my tongue to ask if she was okay, but what a dumb question, of course she wasn't okay! Just because she wasn't crying didn't mean she wasn't hurting. My mind clicked into gear. "When is the funeral? Rob is in the hospital so I can't be away for very long, maybe if I flew up for the service and..."

"Laurie, you don't have to do that."

"But it's your father! Of course I'll try to be there."

"No, no, you don't have to." She sighed. "Plus I'll be too busy to pick you up at the airport. It would just complicate things."

"Oh. Okay." A relief, but a let down too. "Were you with him?"

"No. My sister was, and she called me."

Unnerving, her voice; sad but steady. "It's so hard to know what to say at a time like this, but please let me know if I can do anything to help," I said.

"I will."

Impulsively I added, "When things settle down, Meg, we'll try again."

For a moment there was silence, and then she said, "Are you sure?"

"Of course. We can't give up so fast." Feeling bolder, I said, "Now that we know the process, it'll be a breeze."

"Oh, Laurie, thanks! I'll tell Patrick."

While Meg's frozen embryos waited, I resumed monitoring my cycle in order to determine when I was ovulating; a tedious, inconclusive process that involved buying kits and peeing on sticks for five days in a row. Inexplicably, according to the results, I failed to ovulate for the month of October. I was trying to figure it out when the phone rang. "Hello?"

"Laurie, it's Rob. I have cytomegolovirus. CMV."

"What is it?"

"It's a virus like herpes. Most people have it but it's dormant their whole lives. But my immune system is shot, so it's either become active, or maybe I contracted it. They don't know. It doesn't really matter how I got it, I have it. It's actually not a big deal by itself."

"Good."

He took in a deep breath, and for the first time I heard panic in his voice. "Well, here's the bad news, and it's really bad. I can't be around pregnant women because exposure to CMV is really dangerous for unborn babies."

I felt my whole world implode; one of those moments when you realize that no matter how shitty things are, they can always get shittier. I was going to have to choose between getting pregnant, or being with him during his final precious months or weeks. Standing there, still holding the stupid ovulation test booklet, I couldn't even speak.

"I called you as soon as I found out. What are we going to do?" He broke down. "I'm so sorry, Laurie! I'm so sorry!"

If he was going to cry, I couldn't. "Listen," I said, "before we go crazy, let me talk to Dr. Stoller, okay? I'm sure there are measures I can take to protect myself. I'll wear gloves and a mask."

"Really?"

"Of course! There's not one thing on this planet that could keep me from your side. I'm going to be with you always. Okay?"

"Okay." Small, scared voice.

"I'll call Dr. Stoller right now. I was going to anyway, I'm not ovulating."

"You're not?"

"No."

"Geeze. And I thought *I* had problems."

We managed to laugh; we always did. But as soon as we hung up, I sank to the floor, trembling all over, sick and scared. I knew that Rob, alone in his hospital room, felt the same way.

"I'm not going to tell you that you can't visit him if you get pregnant," Dr. Stoller said.

"You're not?" I asked, stunned. "His doctor said it

would be dangerous for the baby."

"It would be. If my wife was pregnant I wouldn't let her near someone with CMV."

"So why..."

"Because your brother is dying. I make it a point not to get involved in the personal lives of my patients. But if I were you, I would think good and hard about trying to get pregnant right now."

I thanked him and hung up and cried. Cried and cried and cried, a torrent of misery; loud, shoulder-shaking sobs. It was everything - Rob being in the hospital, losing the baby, not ovulating, Meg so far away, and now, the CMV. But most of all it was Dr. Stoller saying out loud that my brother was dying.

"Laurie, I want you to do something for me."

"Of course, Rob, what is it?"

"Will you go to New York and buy another Hirschfeld print for me?"

"Why? You already have one that you never framed. You never even unwrapped it."

"I know, but I bought it for me. I want you to buy another one for someone else."

"Why?"

"I need two. I want to leave one to you and one to Lisa."

I swallowed hard and blinked back tears, for once glad we were on the phone so he couldn't see me. "Rob, you don't need to buy something to give it away. What we'll treasure are the little things you owned, and our memories. You're already leaving us with so much..." I stopped, because suddenly he was crying too hard to hear me. Not unhappy crying like the day we stood in my hallway and held each other, but desperate, hysterical, hopeless sobbing as he realized he truly was going to die. A terrifying moment. More than anything I wanted to say, "Relax, you're going to be fine!" but now was not the time to be dishonest. Softly, I cried with him.

Our conversations, while frequent, grew shorter each time, with my mother or Lisa reaching for the phone to take over while Rob retreated miserably to the aid of his oxygen mask. Twice I called and he couldn't talk at all.

"He's writing a note," my mother said. I heard her sigh. "He says, *Laurie seems so far away.*"

"That's it," I said, "I'm coming to see him."

She lowered her voice. "Hurry."

I called the airlines and booked a flight for the next afternoon, then Ken, to let him know, then Joanne to see if she could watch the kids. I put off making the hardest call until that evening.

"Of course go see him! That's the most important thing!" Meg said.

"I'm so sorry."

"Don't say sorry! We've got plenty of time."

And Rob doesn't. I wiped away tears. "Know what blows my mind, Meg?"

"What."

"Well Rob always says that everything happens for a reason. A million times I've heard him say that. And I keep thinking that if I'd gotten pregnant, I wouldn't be able to see him. And I really think this is it... he's so weak, and he's having so much trouble breathing..."

"Get him a puzzle."

"What?"

"Believe me when I say I know from experience - when you're totally focused on your breathing, it makes breathing even harder. You're using so much energy thinking *am I going to get a deep breath? Or will it just be shallow? How long can I go without breathing? What if I just stop breathing?* And before you know it you're in the middle of a panic attack, and then you can't breath at all. But if you're working on a puzzle, you're focused on something besides your breathing. Try it."

"I'll call my mother right now and have her get him one."

The Missing Piece of the Puzzle

On the plane headed to New Jersey, I shut my eyes and leaned my head back while miles blurred by. November 15th and exactly one year to the day since Meg and I had decided to have a baby. The Universe's idea of a joke? That day felt so long ago.

I took a shuttle from the airport to the hospital, and hurried down the hallway, my suitcase trailing after me, threatening to tip over in my haste. When I reached Rob's room, I stood in the doorway and stared: my mother and father, who hadn't spoken but a few words in years, hunched side by side over a newly-begun jigsaw puzzle. Rob, cross legged at the head of the bed, was examining a piece, and Lisa was saying, "How the heck do *I* know if it's trees or grass? It's green!"

I laughed. They all looked up at the same time and saw me. Rob's face lit up. "Laurie!"

"Hi, guys! No, don't get up!" I said when no one did; no one wanted to disrupt the puzzle. It was *so* weird, seeing my parents together, acting so friendly, but I tried to sound casual as I greeted them both with hugs, then Lisa, then Rob. I was shocked at the change in his condition, he looked horrible; holding him, I could feel him struggling to breathe. He had small oxygen tubes in his nose, but kept reaching for the mask to supplement. Eyes gaunt, skin grayish-yellow, and an expression of fear that I hadn't seen before. Keeping my voice bright, I asked how everyone was.

"No one can think about anything but this stupid puzzle," Lisa said. "Sit down and start working."

And sure enough, that puzzle consumed everyone for the next four days. My dad brought in a large shallow box to contain it, and little by little a serene scene of a rustic footbridge over a sparkling lily-laden brook emerged. Every night one of us spent the night in the other bed in Rob's room, keeping vigil over the puzzle, ensuring that it didn't get knocked over or lose pieces to the cleaning lady's dry mop. On my night there I didn't sleep at all, just lay in bed with him and tried to comfort him.

"I don't think the antibiotics are working this time," he whispered.

"Well there are plenty of others."

"No, Laurie, there are only three for pneumocystis, and this is the last one. Nothing has helped. I'm *so* scared. I didn't think I would be, but I am."

"What are you scared of?"

"That I won't be able to breathe. That I'll suffocate. I don't want to die that way!" He clung to me and cried; a lot of that night was spent crying. Around 2:00 A.M. he asked if I thought all the pieces of the puzzle were there.

"I'm sure they are."

"What if they're not? What if we get to the end and a piece is missing?"

I kissed his head - damp with sweat even though he shivered with cold. "If a piece is missing, I'll call the company."

Reaching for his oxygen mask, he sucked in deep greedy gulps of air. "If you call the company, how long before they send the piece out? How will you describe which piece we need?"

"I'd have them send the whole puzzle. But I'm sure all the pieces are there." His obsession freaked me out, but I recognized it was just a way of thinking about something besides dying. "Want to work on it right now?"

"No, my eyes are tired. You can, though."

Working on a puzzle at 2:00 in the morning was outstandingly high on my list of things I *didn't* want to do, but I carefully brought the box over to the bed and pretended to fit pieces in until at last he slept.

Ken, Mike and Sarah came down for the weekend. I met them in the hospital lobby, hugged and kissed them, then said to the kids, "When you see Uncle Rob you might be surprised at the way he looks."

"What do you mean?" Mike asked.

"Well you know he's been really sick. So he's thin. And he uses a mask to help himself breathe."

"Like a Halloween mask?"

"No. It's just over his nose and mouth. Do you think you can be okay with him looking different?"

"Yes."

"Because it would really hurt his feelings if you acted like you were shocked or scared or something. Do you think you can just go in and say hello? He's the same Uncle Rob, he just looks different."

"I don't care what he looks like," Mike said.

I looked at Ken. He nodded. "I gave him this talk too. He's good. He'll be fine."

He was. He walked into the room and went right over to Rob's bed. "Sarah and I have our own puzzles," he said proudly. "We can do ours while you do yours."

"That's fantastic," said Rob. "What's yours of?"

"A horse. Sarah's is a dog."

"I gotta bridge," Rob said in a rueful tone that made Mike laugh.

"Is it boring?"

"No, it's okay. A horse sounds fun, though."

Mike was too young to really understand what was going on, he'd only been told that Uncle Rob was sick. But something in his heart realized there was more to it than that, and so he said helpfully, "The next puzzle you do, you should do with a horse."

Rob smiled. "I'm not sure they'll let a horse in the hospital, but we can try."

"A horse!" said Sarah. Wiggling in my arms she wasn't aware of the gloomy dynamics, all she knew was that her favorite people were in one room. I let her down and she hugged Lisa and Mom-Mom and Pop-Pop. Then she went up to Rob and said, "How come you're still in bed?"

"Lazybones." He reached out and got in a tickle before she giggled and backed off.

"These puzzles aren't going to do themselves," I announced. "Come on, you guys." I set the kids up with their puzzles on the other bed, and Ken and I joined the adults.

After about an hour Rob sat back, stretched, and looked at everyone. We fell silent, waiting. He was our barometer - if he was fine, we were fine; if he was scared, we were scared.

"Somehow," he said, "I didn't picture it ending this way."

Solemnly, we digested his words. It was the first time any of us had referred to the end, and I think we were half expecting him to lie back, shut his eyes, and pass away peacefully, like in a movie.

"I think it's kinda fun," Mike said.

We smiled, then we laughed, then we really laughed. Rob started to cough, and as he reached for his oxygen mask he managed to say, "Yeah, this is a blast alright!"

On Sunday I drove back to Rhode Island with Ken and the kids. My mother called me late that night to say she and Rob had finished the puzzle. But then she called again a few hours later, this time in hysterics. "Robert couldn't breathe and they put him on a respirator!"

"Oh no!"

"They're hoping that if he can hang on, the antibiotics will start to work. He's in the ICU. Laurie, can you come back? Right away?"

"I'll be there as soon as I can."

When I stepped out of the elevator onto the ICU floor, I was surprised to see my mother standing at the nurses' station, waiting for me.

"Oh thank God!" She hugged me, crying so hard that I thought he must have already died. But she said, "Lisa is with him."

"Is he awake?"

"I don't think so. He hasn't opened his eyes."

"Where's Dad?"

"Getting everyone coffee." She took my hand and walked me to the ICU. "Only two visitors at a time. Go on in, I'll wait here for your father."

"Okay." With a deep breath, I went in. But nothing could have prepared me for the sight of him lying already corpse-like, bloated and distorted, his arms like over-stuffed sausages, with veins popping and needles buried in skin, and tubes in his lungs draining bloodied yellow fluid. A thick tube down his throat propped his mouth open. "Oh my God!"

"Oh, look, Rob," Lisa said, "Laurie is here."

Leaning over, I gently kissed the pale, taught forehead; noticed a sour unwashed clean smell that made me sad, he'd always been so fastidious. "Hi, Rob. How are you doing?" Of course there was no answer. "Do you think he can hear us?" I asked her quietly.

She nodded. "His vitals are strong, and he's getting morphine, so he's not in any pain."

I kissed him again. "I have to go make a phone call. I'll be right back, okay?"

"A phone call! What kinda excuse is that to leave?" Lisa joked bravely, but the tilt of her head said, *Tell Ken to get here as soon as he can.*

Leaving the kids with my grandmother, Ken joined us for day after horrendous day in the grim ICU. I was stunned by how many visitors sat with us in the waiting room - clients and business associates, dozens of friends, including some he hadn't seen in years, his high school English teacher, the hospital cleaning lady, even two nurses from his previous hospital floor who regaled us with stories of his grace and courage.

After a week, Ken took the kids back to Rhode Island, with the promise to return as soon as I needed him.

"I can't do this anymore," announced my mother on the evening of December 18th as we drove home from the hospital. "I can't stand seeing him like this. I don't want to go back into that room."

"It's okay. I'm sure he'll understand."

"You don't think he'll be... hurt?"

"Mom, no! You showed your love for him in a thousand ways. And not wanting to see him like this is just another way. You've already said goodbye to him."

"Okay." She sighed. "Know what tomorrow is?"

"Yours and Dad's anniversary."

"We'll spend it together for the first time in eight years. Leave it to Robert!"

We smiled together. I put my hand on her arm, trying to imagine what she was going through, losing her child. I couldn't bear thinking about Michael or Sarah lying in that ICU. As bad as my pain was, hers had an intensity I hoped I'd never know.

Rob never regained consciousness. Lisa and I kept telling him it was okay to go, that it was time for his spirit to be free, and on December 19th she and my dad and I held our final tearful vigil. As we watched, his vital signs grew weaker, his breaths slowed down, and at five minutes to midnight he drew his last, and was gone. A nurse came in, shut off the machines, and in a kind voice, said to take all the time we needed. Another doctor called over as soon as he heard the news, expressed his sympathy, and then reminded us that Rob's possessions, including the puzzle, were in ICU storage.

We took turns kissing him; I lingered with my lips pressed against the back of his hand. Until they took him from the room it felt like he was still a little bit with us. Then, in a daze, we packed up his clothes, cards, all the silly little things people had brought. The completed puzzle was meticulously placed between two pieces of cardboard with edges taped, and put carefully into the trunk of my mother's car.

But when we got to her house and opened it up on the dining room table, we discovered a piece was missing. Weeks of worry and no sleep, of having to be brave, of having to spend every day in the hospital, of putting our lives on hold for so long flooded everyone like a tsunami, and we went completely ballistic.

"Where is it?" demanded Lisa angrily, "you didn't tape it up enough!"

"All the edges were taped! It's when we put it into your mother's trunk! She had all that stuff in there! It wasn't lying flat!" said my dad.

I was on my hands and knees, searching under the table. "Everyone *calm down*! It's gotta be here!"

"I'm going to call the hospital," announced my mother, reaching for the phone. "I'll tell them to look for it in the ICU. Maybe they can send someone out to the parking lot to look."

Dashing to the door to see if it had fallen out on the way to the table, I wondered if we'd ever look back on this and laugh. "Mom, give me the keys to your trunk - I'm going to look there."

We all went out; no one spoke. I put in the key, the trunk rose open, everyone's eyes searched. Lisa snapped, "It's not *here*! We have to go back to the hospital! Mom, *call* them!"

"Look!" My dad pointed, and we all saw it at the same time, the tiny corner sticking out from under the trunk's dark gray carpet. I reached in and grabbed it. We filed silently inside like some bizarre royal procession, me at the head clutching the priceless treasure. Then, with the last piece of the puzzle in place, we stood with heads bowed and hearts breaking from the horrible reality of knowing we would never see him again... never hear his laugh, never look into his beautiful eyes, never feel his loving gaze upon us. But sorrow blended with relief because we knew his long, painful battle was finally over.

Rob's jigsaw puzzle.

Robert Kaufman

"Death will come to us all, but life is only there if we choose to live it. I chose to live mine the only way I knew how. People said I was brave, but it was not my courage that got me through the last eight years, but the support of my family and friends. Living with AIDS was the easy part; the hard part was leaving. The disease that has overtaken my body never took my spirit or my desire to go on. It taught me about life and how to live out the balance of mine. I was not my disease, but I would not have been me without it. AIDS took away my choices, but showed me my options. All of you still have choices. Learn from my lack of them, and choose the path that makes you whole. And remember - I will see you again and be with you always."

Robert Kaufman
December 28, 1962 - December 19, 1994

Part Two

Wrap a Quilt Around It

My grief was brutal and unrelenting for months. I got the kids up and fed, sent Mike to school, played with Sarah, and each evening over supper listened with a convincingly attentive smile to Ken's account of his day. On weekends I tried to organize family activities, which I performed mechanically, without passion or interest.

"Rob would hate seeing you like this," Ken said.

"I know."

"He'd be so pissed."

"I know."

"He'd say you have it all and you should be enjoying it."

The old me would have snapped, "I *know!*" but I only had enough energy to sigh.

Ken sighed too; would have preferred a fight to this gloom. "What about joining a support group?"

"I'm not ready to feel better yet. You have to want to feel better."

"Maybe it'll help you get to that point."

"But I can't *be* at that point, because I'm not *at* that point," I said, now getting annoyed. What about that didn't he understand?

"I agree with Ken," Joanne said. "You need help."

Her betrayal stung. "I have no desire to stand up in front of a bunch of teary-eyed strangers pouring out my sad story and have them say *That's nothing, listen to what I went through!*"

"Maybe it wouldn't be like that. Maybe you'd be in a room full of other depressed people, and you can all agree that life really sucks sometimes, and then someone will say something funny, and you'll laugh. You know, no one expects you to heal all at once. It happens in baby steps." She put her hand on my arm. "At least get Mike help," she said gently.

I looked away, too ashamed to face her. I had tried talking to him a few times, but he was shut down. And how could I help him when I was such a mess? I saw to his needs, but I wasn't *there* for him, I wasn't present during any of our conversations or play time.

As if reading my mind she said, "You've been through such a lot, don't beat yourself up for not being the world's best Mom right now. But you have to get it together, for him, for Ken, for your marriage, for everyone who counts on you."

"No pressure," I grumbled. But I knew she was right. "I'll check into it today. Mike and I will both go."

"Good. Sarah seems fine?"

"Yeah. Because Rob visits her."

"What?"

"She says he visits her. At night. They dance." Ridiculously, I started to cry - these days it didn't take much to set me off. "I want a sign from him, Joanne! I would feel so much better if I could get some kind of sign!"

"A sign of what?"

"I don't know... that his soul still exists."

"You know it does. The love you shared, that'll never die."

"I know, but I still want a sign," I said, angry and stubborn.

"That would really make you feel better?"

I nodded, sniffed back tears.

"Okay," she said, "let's start looking for one."

Hospice offered groups for adults and kids, so I signed us up for Wednesday evenings. We were both nervous on the first night, and talked about it on the ride over. I admired his guts - he didn't want to go, but knew he had to, and didn't argue. Reluctantly, I dropped him off with a very sweet-looking woman named Mrs. Oakley and six kids who were about his age. He walked in and sat, exchanging unhappy glances with another boy.

"He's going to be fine," Mrs. Oakley assured me as she escorted me to the door. "I won't make him talk unless he wants to. They start out shy, and the next thing you know they're verbalizing their emotions and all the kids are saying, *Me too! Me too!* Knowing they're not alone makes them feel so much better. We have fun, too. Lots of games and art projects."

I nodded, loitered, blinked back tears of guilt.

"Even the best parents can't protect kids from pain," she said. "You did the right thing, bringing him here."

"He was very close to his Uncle Rob. My brother."

"I understand." She held up a file, which obviously held the information I'd given during my initial phone call. "I'm going to take very good care of him. And you'll be just up the hall." *GO*, said her eyes. With a final look at him, I left to find my group.

"Welcome," said the facilitator, an ex-hippie in his

sixties with long gray hair in a pony tail, beard, moustache, and a pendant that looked like an oriental letter. "I'm Sam. Help yourself to coffee. We'll start in a few minutes."

The coffee looked and smelled institutional, but I poured myself a cup anyway because everyone else was having some and I wanted to fit in with the group of four women and one man, all of whom were laughing and chatting with ease. The chairs were arranged in a circle and as I sat, Sam took the seat next to me. The others sat too, all the while regarding me with kind smiles.

"This is Laurie," said Sam.

Everyone murmured, "Hi Laurie," and I felt the urge to stand and confess something disgraceful: *"I'm Laurie... I like to set small animals on fire..."* "Hi," I said.

"Laurie just lost her brother after a long illness, so maybe she'll tell us about that in a bit. But first, Angela, how was your father's surgery?"

Grateful not to be the focus of attention yet, I caught up with the dynamics: Angela's elderly mother had just passed away, and now her father was very sick. Steve's wife died after a three-year battle with breast cancer. Julia and Cindy were dealing with the deaths of their husbands, also from cancer. Ellie, like me, was mourning a brother. I realized right away that no one was there to complain. Friendships had formed based on a desire to support and be supported. By the time Sam turned to me, I was ready to talk about Rob. I was tearful, but for once didn't break down, and they were good listeners who didn't interrupt to ask for personal details: *Where did he get AIDS? Did his partner have AIDS too? Is he dead? Have you been tested?* Sam talked about the process of grieving, how it was different for everyone. Most of the deaths had been the result of disease, but Ellie's brother had died in a car accident. She hadn't endured the weeks or months of suffering like we had, but she hadn't gotten the chance to say goodbye. We talked about our reactions - some had breakdowns, others, like me, wallowed. Steve shut off all his emotions, and Ellie admitted that she was mad at God.

The hour passed quickly. I thanked everyone, said I'd see them next week, and picked up Mike from his group.

"I liked it," he said even before I asked.

We headed down the hall toward the exit. "What did you like about it?"

"I just liked it. One kid, Billy, his mom died." Mike's hand found mine and held tight. "He cried."

"That must be really hard for him."

"Uh huh."

"Did you talk about Uncle Rob?"

"Yeah, I said he was funny and I missed him. But he was real sick, Mom. He wasn't happy living at the hospital."

"No," I said, "he wasn't."

"We had cookies and juice. Melissa is diabetic so she just hadda apple. The cookies weren't as good as yours, but they were still good."

In that moment I felt my sadness lift. It didn't disappear, and it wasn't as if I wanted to kick up my heels and shout hurrah. But a gentle peace slipped in and found its way back to my heart. Mike and I would continue to attend the support groups for a while, but I knew that there was nothing they could say that would help more than the feeling of his sweaty little hand in mine.

Lisa called that night to hear about the group, and after I finished telling her, asked, "Have you heard about the AIDS quilt?"

"Yeah, I've been thinking about it," I said. "but the idea of doing a panel felt so overwhelming and sad. Like it would make me feel worse, not better."

"I felt that way too. But now I think we should."

"I do too, I think it'll help us heal. And It's a great

way to honor him."
   "Mom and I were talking about coming for a visit."
   "When?"
   "Not this weekend, but is next weekend too soon?"
   "No! I'll tell the kids, they'll be so excited!"
   "And we can start working on the panel."

   Researching the AIDS quilt, I learned that it was first conceived in 1985 by San Francisco gay activist Cleve Jones as a way to commemorate AIDS casualties. It was also a dig at the homophobic conservatives; a collision of the very symbol of household coziness and a deadly ·sexually-transmitted disease affecting gay men. Originally placards with names taped to a wall, the project grew as more died. Two years later the first AIDS quilt was displayed on the National Mall in Washington, D.C. After half a million people visited the quilt in one weekend, it went on a 20-city tour and raised $500,000 for research and AIDS-related services. In 1992 the Quilt returned to Washington, now bearing panels from every state, and 28 countries. I contacted the NAMES Project and received the application, which outlined specific parameters for panel size and design, in addition to requiring brief biographies of the person being honored and the quilt makers, which would be photographed and archived.

   "It's perfect," I told Lisa and my mother. Their arrival

an hour before had brought tears and hugs and all of us asking, *"How are you doing, are you okay?"* but now we were sitting at the dining room table drinking coffee and looking at Lisa's design for the quilt. She'd matched Rob's business card with the name Robert S. Kaufman across the top. Beneath the name was a broken heart, and she wanted everyone in the family to contribute prints of their hands to be placed under the heart as if they were reaching up toward it.

"Plus," she said, "some of his friends want to be included, so I was thinking, instead of the checkerboard Rob's card has at the bottom, we could give people a black or white square, and they can put whatever they want on it."

"He would love that! Let's go to the fabric store tomorrow."

"I'll go too," announced Sarah.

We laughed as I scooped her up onto my lap. "Do you know what a fabric store is?"

"Yes!"

"What is it?"

"I don't know."

"Gee, I was hoping you'd stay home with me," my mother said. "I was thinking we could play some games while Mommy and Ti-Ti are gone."

"Games!" agreed Sarah.

The sound of a car pulling into the driveway told us that Ken was home. My gaze went to the clock - before five, just as he promised. I hadn't even begun dinner. Maybe a pizza night?

Sarah wiggled expectantly, and when Ken walked in, shouted "Ti-Ti and Mom-Mom are here!"

"I see!" he grinned. More hugs, and Mike, who'd been in the den watching TV, appeared in the doorway. Sarah slid off my lap to be taken into Ken's arms. Surrounded by my family, I felt contentment... then guilt. This was what Meg wanted, what I had. What I could give her.

"Did they specify the kind of material we need for the background?" Lisa asked as we browsed the bolts of fabric. Back home my mother was probably assembling and disassembling Sarah's Babar puzzle for the twentieth time.

"They said it has to be heavy, like canvas. Duck fabric, I think they called it. I hope it's not too thick to sew stuff onto."

A saleswoman overheard me and said "Duck fabric is in the back, past ribbon."

We thanked her and headed in the direction of her pointed finger. I hadn't mentioned the surrogacy to my mother or Lisa, because I wanted this weekend to be about Rob, but I kept thinking about Meg. We hadn't spoken in a few weeks, and it occurred to me that she and Patrick had probably given up. How many nights had he come home from work and asked, *"Didja hear from Laurie today?"* Had she shaken her head and said, *"No, but I'm sure I will"?* She was probably dying to call, but was afraid it would sound like she was calling, not to find out how I was, but to see if I was going to go through with the baby plans. Poor Meg!

"What about this?" Lisa pulled out a bolt of heavy white. "They have it in black too."

"Looks perfect. How much?"

She located the tag and flipped it over so we could read. We both gasped when we saw the name of the manufacturer: Robert Kaufman. Eyes wide and jaws hanging open, we looked at each other, then back at the tag.

"Oh my God," I whispered. Neither of us spoke as we pulled out the white and black bolts and brought them to the counter to be cut and priced.

The ride home was quiet and solemn. I thought about how much Rob wanted the surrogacy to work, how he had encouraged me each time to try again. I let out a deep breath. "I'm going to call Meg tonight and tell her I'm ready."

Lisa, gripping the bag that held the fabric like it was full of gold coins, looked at me, smiled and nodded. "Good."

Let's Try Again

"Are you sure?" Meg asked.

"Of course! In fact, I'm even more sure now than I was before, and you know how sure I was before."

"How come?"

"Because you lost your dad and I lost my brother. After two deaths it feels right to start a new life. Especially one who will carry the blood of your father and my brother." My voice broke a little as I thought about the importance of what I was saying.

"And Ken is okay with you trying again?"

"He's a little more nervous this time, but he said if it's what I want to do, then I should do it. And Mike and Sarah need to see that life goes on, even when you're sad."

"That sure is true."

"This time it's going to work," I promised. "This time the baby has two guardian angels. So go ahead and be excited!"

She laughed. "Okay, I'll tell Patrick!"

"Of course I worry," I told Joanne later that day.

"That it won't work?"

"That I'm doing this for the wrong reason."

"Which is...?"

"What if I'm only doing this because of the hole in my

life that Rob left when he died?"

"Well so what if you are? I mean it's still a fantastic thing that you're doing, and Meg will have her dream come true because of you."

"But what if I think that by doing this, it'll somehow fill that hole, and then what if, after it's all over, the hole is still there? What if it's like this endless, bottomless pit that can never be filled? No matter what I do or who I'm with?" I sighed. "Stop me as soon as I show symptoms of over analyzing everything."

She smiled, but in a sort of somber way, respectful of my angst. "Here's what I think," she said. "You're grieving. You're nervous. You have a ton of pressure on you. You're trying to intellectualize your emotions. Why not just feel them, instead of trying to label them or justify them? You wanted to do this before Rob died, and you still want to do it. For whatever reason, this is something you *want* to do. When it's over and Meg has her baby, can you honestly sit there and tell me there's a chance you'll regret doing it?"

I shook my head.

"There you go."

So back I plunged into the world of menstruation, ovulation, and phone calls with Meg. In May on day 15 of my cycle I tested myself twice to confirm it was time for another trip to IVF Canada.

Meg picked me up at the airport. The sight of her triggered exhaustion, as if my body remembered what it had been through last time it was with her.

"Welcome back!" she said, hugging me. "You have a 3:00 appointment at the clinic to have blood drawn."

"I'm fine, thanks, how are you?"

"Glad you're here, that's how I am!"

"Me too." I just had a carry on bag, so there was no need to retrieve luggage. "Hey," I said as we headed toward the exit, "sorry it took me so long to come to this decision. I'm sure you and Patrick were waiting on pins and needles."

She shrugged as she foraged through her purse for keys. "We haven't really been thinking about it much. We figured you didn't want to try again."

I stopped walking. "You thought I wouldn't try again, and not even tell you?"

She stopped walking too, caught off guard by my disbelieving tone. "Well, I mean, after what you went through, we just assumed..."

"Meg! Obviously I'm going to tell you my decision either way! I wouldn't just not say a word!" Usually I didn't care that we were so different, but this was basic courtesy! If the situation was reversed and she changed her mind about carrying my baby, she wouldn't have told me? I felt aggravated, as if that had actually happened.

"We didn't expect you to feel you had to let us know. We never would have wanted you to have any extra pressure on you," she explained, apologetic and sincere.

I sighed, felt bad now; resumed walking. "Maybe I'm a little edgy."

"You have every right to be." She was silent for a moment, then added, "I guess I'm just not good at saying what's on my mind, the way you are."

"What's on your mind *right now*?"

"Lunch," she grinned. When I didn't laugh, she said, "Just how grateful I am to you for doing this. And how scared I am to hope that it'll work this time. I don't want to get all worked up about it and have it not work."

"It *will* work," I said.

"Yes, but you can't *know* that. You're just being positive."

"And you're just being negative." I shook my head, tried to lighten up. "I guess we're just being ourselves."

"Don't be upset, okay?"

"Okay." We reached her car and got in. "I meant to ask you, do you know how they defrost the embryos?"

She slipped on sunglasses and backed out of the parking space. "I asked Dr. Lee. It's *very* scientific, Laur. I doubt you'll be able to understand it."

"Oh?"

"I mean, I could *try* to explain..."

"I wanna know," I said.

"Well...." she drew out the word, then took in a deep breath. "Okay. They take the embryos out of the freezer."

"Uh huh?"

"And set them on a counter."

"Uh huh?"

"And then they wait for them to defrost." She glanced over with a mischievous smile. "Do you need me to explain it again?"

I stared. "They take them out of the freezer and put them on the counter to defrost?"

"Uh huh."

"Like hamburger?"

"Exactly."

"Huh." We laughed, picturing it. Then I said, "So they're going to defrost two of them?"

"Yes."

"What did you decide to do with the others?"

"Well, Patrick was dead set against donation. I was on the fence at first, but then he made me realize how weird it would be - a sibling of the child we're trying to create running around the world without our knowledge. I mean, what would you have done?"

"I would have donated them."

"Well, we thought that would be weird." She glanced at me, looking defensive. "Maybe you'd feel different if it was you making the decision."

"Maybe," I lied.

Two days later, which happened to be Mother's Day, the clinic called to let us know the embryos were thawed and ready for implantation, and at 11:01 on Monday morning, resplendent in my hospital johnny, I climbed onto the table. Meg, who had come into the room with me, kept me company by reading a fashion quiz from a magazine. She got a higher score because she had actually thrown out her clothes from the 1980s. But when Dr. Lee failed to appear after 45 minutes we both started getting nervous.

"I can't miss my flight! Even if he does this right now, there's no time for me to lie inverted for an hour."

"I'll go ask the nurse." She disappeared. Alone, chilly, I jiggled both feet, chewed my fingernails, worst case scenario'd, and made myself crazy.

"You're not going to believe this!" said Meg as she returned, "Dr. Lee is at lunch!"

"What?"

"*He's at lunch!*"

"Can someone else do the transfer?"

"There's no one else on today. They paged him. I told him you have to catch a flight, he said he'd be here ASAP."

I lay back, trying not to see it as a bad omen. We waited, fretful now, no longer chatty and excited. When he arrived a few minutes later he said he was so sorry, he completely forgot, he had never forgotten a patient before, this was a first! I wanted to scream *"Do the transfer now, apologize later!"* but, like Meg, managed to be polite. He tilted the table to a 45-degree angle, and with a syringe, injected the embryos.

"Okay, all done!" He glanced at his watch. "Tell you what. Lie inverted for fifteen minutes, then you can go."

"Are you sure?" Meg asked.

He nodded. "I told you, I'm convinced it doesn't matter either way. Like Laurie said, women get pregnant all the time without lying at an angle."

We thanked him, and he left. I lay inverted for the fifteen minutes, got dressed, and Meg and I returned to the waiting room.

Patrick looked up, relieved, and stood. "How'd it go?"

I touched my belly. "All systems go."

His eyes were on Meg, who, I suddenly noticed, seemed distraught. I touched her arm. "Are you okay?"

Her eyes glistening with tears, she nodded. "I have to use the ladies room, I'll be right back."

Alarmed, I watched her hurry off, then turned to Patrick for an explanation.

"She's been really tense lately," he said. "All those months of not knowing what your plans were, I guess it kind of wore on her after a while."

In shock, I couldn't come up with one single thing to say, not one single thing. So many emotions ran through me - concern for Meg, anger at Patrick for saying such a manipulative thing to make me feel guilty, and hurt that I'd been lied to, either by her when she said she hadn't been thinking about it much, or by him. In any other set of circumstances I would have confronted him. But he was not just my best friend's husband; he was the father to be of the child I was now potentially carrying. I stood in silence until she returned. Her cheeks were bright red, as if she'd splashed hot water on her face.

"What's going on?" I asked.

She laughed. "I just felt this rush of, I don't know, I just needed to cry. I have no idea why. You're the one being shot up with hormones and I'm the one who falls apart."

Patrick put his arm around her and kissed the top of her head. I couldn't even look at him.

"Are you sure that's all it is? Because if something's bothering you ..."

"I'm sure. Honest. It just came over me and I didn't want to cry out here."

Like a stern mother, I made her face me. She smiled brightly, seemed fine. Next I looked at Patrick; our eyes met, then he turned away.

"Well," said Ken when I told him that night, "you know how overprotective he is. Maybe he really thought that; maybe he wasn't lying, maybe he really didn't know it was just nerves or whatever."

"But even if it was true, why say it to me? After I've traveled all the way to Canada to get shot up with his DNA? It made me feel sick."

"I agree, that was an insensitive thing to say. But that's what he's like - rough around the edges."

Consoled by his mellow tone, and grateful that he was on my side, I decided to let it go. Probably when Patrick said the months of waiting had gotten to Meg, he meant they'd gotten to *him*.

My shots with Dr. Stoller resumed within a week. Maybe it was psychological but the sight of him made me gag. But when I felt nauseous in the deli section of the supermarket on the way home, I began to wonder if it was more. The first in a series of pregnancy tests, which took place the Friday of Memorial Day weekend, indicated that I was 15 on the Quantum Beta scale. I was told it was the low side of negative. No one seemed to know what that meant, it felt like I was a little pregnant. There wasn't much I could do but wait for the next test, which would take place in five days.

That weekend Rob's two best friends stopped by on their way to Boston, which was fun but painful, and it seemed like at least one person was in tears at all times. They loved the idea for the AIDS Quilt panel, and left with squares to decorate. It was almost a relief to see them drive away Sunday afternoon. I'd been feeling more and more nauseated, and had barely tolerated last night's spaghetti dinner.

On May 30th I took another blood test. My HCG, which was 15 on the 26th, was supposed to double every two days, meaning it should be at least 60.

I tore home and called Meg. "A hundred and sixty-six!"

"A hundred and sixty-six?"

"We're pregnant!"

"Oh Laurie! How do you feel?"

"Like puking! But in a good way."

We laughed together. I knew she was eager to call Patrick so I told her we'd talk later, and hung up. I needed to go across the street and pick up Sarah, but wanted some alone time to luxuriate in the success. *I did it! I did it!* Feeling humble and powerful at the same time, I wandered out to the patio, then stopped in the doorway. My hand went to my heart and tears filled my eyes. Cheerful purple and yellow blossoms lined the edge of the garden wall. Robert's violas.

Back to shots, hormones, crying spells, unrelenting nausea, and eventually a ferocious craving for salt, specifically, roast beef. Recalling the delicious New York style sandwiches from my youth, I called my mother one evening and begged her to have one prepared and sent to me. She took my order, and called back in a few minutes: the sandwich would be $7.95, but the deli wanted to charge $30 to ship it!

"Okay, pass," I sighed.

"I set up an ultrasound for July 16th," I told Joanne. "Meg and Patrick are coming down for it. They seemed really excited!"

"I bet!"

"I'm so glad they understand the need for them to be involved. And this is really important."

"I know! First chance to see the baby!" She sighed. "I remember my first ultra sound when I was pregnant with Eric. Nothing beat the thrill of seeing that little blob!"

"When I had my first, the doctor kept saying *Right there! See? Right there! Look right there!* I couldn't see anything!"

"Neither could John! He was so annoyed! At one point he accused me of just pretending to be able to see it."

Mothers' memories; we laughed. It made me so happy to think that soon Meg would have them too.

"All the tests look good," Dr. Stoller said. "Feel like having the ultrasound right now? We just got a new portable machine... I'm dying to try it out. Want to?"

I hesitated a long time. I wanted Meg to be there for the first official look. On the other hand, it would provide such peace of mind to know that everything was fine... even though I knew everything was fine... to *really* know would be so great... that way if there were any surprises, we'd know about them beforehand, and she wouldn't have to -

"Any day now," Dr. Stoller said.

"Okay, let's do it."

So he wheeled it over and I lifted my johnny and endured the icy jelly chill. Eyes locked on the monitor, he said, "Looks good, Laurie. This time it's right where it belongs!"

Thank God! Even though I knew it was fine, to *really* know it was fine...

"I feel horrible," I told Ken as soon as the kids were in bed.

"Why?"

"I feel so guilty! Maybe I should have waited for Meg. Do you think I should have?"

"I think you did the right thing. Just don't tell her."

"I won't! I just wanted to make sure everything…"

"Was fine. I know. You told me ten thousand times." He kissed me on the nose. "She never needs to know."

"Bad news, Laurie," Meg said. "Patrick and I might not be able to come down for the ultrasound."

"What? Why?"

"He's having a lot of issues with the business right now. I thought I would just come by myself, but it's so hard for me to travel alone."

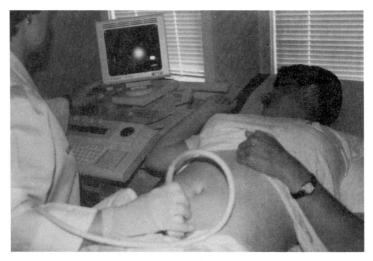

Laurie's first ultrasound.

Oh Meg! You have to come!"

"I know, I wanted to. But the thing is, the only reason we need the ultrasound now is because IVF needs to know how big the baby is. So you go ahead and have Dr. Stoller contact them with the information."

"IVF? I thought the ultrasound was for you guys!"

"No. I mean, we'd love to be there and see it. But the main reason was for IVF."

"Why didn't you tell me?"

"What difference does it make?"

"Because I already had it!"

"What?"

"Dr. Stoller really wanted to do it," I said carefully and more or less truthfully, "I mean, after what happened last time..."

"I can understand him wanting to do it, but why would you lie about it?"

"I didn't lie!"

"You pretended that you didn't have it already! That's lying!"

"I only did it because…"

"I'm going nuts trying to figure out how I can manage this trip, not because I need to be there, but because you want me there, and then you sneak off and do it without telling me! And then you act like you didn't, just so I'll still come down! God, Laurie! You know, some of us can't just jump on a plane at the drop of a hat! I have a million things going on here. Plus you know how hard it is for me to get around."

The sound of her voice, her indignation, her *boo hoo, poor me!* was so infuriating that for several seconds I couldn't speak or breathe. Forcing myself to stay calm, I said, "I didn't realize what an inconvenience the trip was for you. I thought you were excited about the baby and wanted to be part of the process. If you had told me that all you cared about were the numbers, I wouldn't have suggested you come down."

"Suggested? You practically begged me!"

"I did not!"

"You did so! You said, *Oh Meg, you have to be here for the first ultrasound!*"

"Because you should want to be here for it! Any normal woman would!" I could tell by her silence that it was a direct hit: Cold Bitch Felled by Brutal Truth. "I don't understand you," I said, more unhappy now than mad. "Why wouldn't you want to see the baby?"

She sighed. "I do. Honest. It's just that Patrick is so stressed out by work that he comes home every night in such a bad mood. When I asked if he could take a few days off to fly down, he looked at me like I was crazy. I was afraid to bring it up again, and so I guess I talked myself into believing I didn't want to go either. I'm sorry." She started to cry, her breath ragged gasps.

"It's okay," I said quickly, worried that she was going to choke, "I would have done that too. Okay? Stop crying."

"I was so mean to you, I'm so sorry!"

"Really, it's okay!" I felt bad, but in a way I was glad it happened; it was a good reminder of her condition and why I was doing this. "Anyway, you haven't asked me about the results of the ultrasound."

She sniffled, tried to recover. "What were they?"

"That we have a perfect little baby!"

"Oh, Laurie!" Joy restored, her voice brightened. "Thank God!"

"That oughta cheer Patrick up. Don't tell him what happened, you know, with us."

"No, I won't, I'll just give him the good news. I'll call him now."

"You okay?"

"Yes! Thanks, Laurie! I love you!"

"I love you too."

Quickening

"There's no way to say this nicely," Joanne began.

I held up my hand. "I know. I look horrible. My boobs are down to my waist, and my ass is taking over the house."

"You need to get new clothes. Isn't Meg sending you money?"

I sighed. "She told me to buy stuff and send the receipts. I haven't yet. It would be so much easier if she'd come here and take me shopping."

A good friend who didn't like to judge, Joanne said nothing, just started chopping onions to put in her potato salad for the barbeque we were having that night. Watching her, I was relieved that the smell didn't make me sick.

"Did I tell you she got the picture from the ultrasound? She loved it. She said she could see the baby right away. It took Patrick a little while. Her little jelly bean."

"That had to make her feel good."

"I'm sure. Hey, wanna hear something weird?"

"Always."

"Well she told me they were going to Ray and Sally's house for dinner tonight. Ray and Sally are their best friends for years. They've gone on trips together and stuff."

"Uh huh?"

"So I asked her if she was going to tell them, and she said she didn't know."

Joanne's eyebrows raised. "Her best friends don't even know?"

"Told you it was weird. She finally told her sister."

Outside I could hear Ken's voice: *"No running near the pool, Sarah!"* A million times a day I ached to talk about the pregnancy with Rob. He would have insisted upon hearing every detail, even the gross ones, like how many days between decent bowel movements. Mike wasn't going to the support groups anymore, but I was; talking about Rob's death in group made not talking about it to anyone else bearable. Sometimes I was fine; other times the pain hit me like it was fresh, like no time had passed at all, like I was never going to heal. *"Sarah, no running!"*

"Why don't men know that if you're dealing with a three-year old you can't just tell them to stop something, you have to physically stop them?" Joanne wondered as she took celery from the refrigerator.

"I have no idea." My conversation with Meg had ended on a sour note, with me commenting that I was still surprised that no one had to take psychological tests but me, and her getting defensive: *"You think I need one?"*

"Ken taking you anywhere special for your birthday?" Joanne asked.

"No, but compared to what I did last year anything is special." Looking away, I squeezed out a few tears. Last year Rob had been alive.

Meg agreed to come with me when I had the amniocentesis on August 17th. I was looking forward to seeing her until I got a call from Ken saying that his parents were coming the weekend before, and the visits would overlap. I wanted to be furious with him, but knew it would do no good. So I called her.

"Ugh!" she said. "Do they know I'll be there?"

"No, Ken was too chicken to tell them. He'll have to call them back tonight."

"Well I'm not afraid of them."

"Because you've never met them."

"Anyway, nothing we can do about it."

That was true. I tried to keep busy. Lisa and I had begun work on the quilt panel, and everyone in the family had made prints of their hands. It was very emotional and I'd feel drained after just an hour or so. But it was therapeutic too, because I could grieve and cry. It was my time with Rob.

As the date of the amniocentesis neared, I started feeling anxious; I wasn't sure if it was because of the 12 inch needle whose destination was my belly, or the visit from my in laws. One morning I couldn't settle down, and I called Meg to chat.

"Is something wrong?" she asked right away.

"No, why?"

"Well you're calling at the most expensive time of day. I mean, if nothing's wrong, why don't you wait until later, when the rates go down? My phone bills are huge, Laur."

Shock and rage swept through me. I took a deep breath. "I'm going to hang up right now, because I am so angry with you, I don't trust myself to stay on the phone." Without giving her a chance to respond, I hung up. Blood boiling, I paced. I called Ken. I called Joanne, my mother, and my sister. Two hours later, not feeling any better, I called Meg. "Just so you know, I'll pay for this one," I said.

"You don't have to be so bitchy. You have no idea how expensive everything is. Patrick is worried that we…"

"You listen to me," I interrupted. "I do know how expensive everything is, because half of what I buy I don't even tell you about."

"Like what?"

Moisturizer for my belly. Tylenol for the pregnancy headaches. A thousand Saltines to settle my stomach. Panty liners. I'm walking around in four-year old maternity clothes that don't even fit. Half the phone calls I make to you I don't even include in the tally."

"Well you're supposed to keep track of…"

"But I don't care about that stuff, Meg. What I can't get over is how you're treating me! I'm not just a warm body having your baby, I've been your friend for twenty years! How dare you insult me like that?"

She didn't answer right away, then said in a subdued, shamed voice, "You're right. I'm sorry. I'm just real stressed about money right now."

"Who isn't!" I practically shouted.

"You're right, you're right! I shouldn't have spoken to you that way. It's just… Patrick makes me crazy. It's no excuse, I know. But he gets so worried that he gets me all worried. I had just gotten off the phone with him when you called. I'm so sorry I said what I did, I wish I could take it back! I love when you call!"

"Didn't sound like it!"

"I know. You're doing this huge huge thing for us, and then I bitch about one stupid phone call. Please don't be mad. Okay? Maybe part of the stress is that we're so far apart. Once we see each other next week, we'll feel better."

"I hope so," I said.

And it *was* better once she got here. We hugged hard, cried, hugged some more. Patrick came too, and seemed relaxed. My in-laws were cold but cordial, and of course said nothing about the arrangement. Thankfully, they left before the amniocentesis.

I watched Meg's face as she saw the baby for the first time on the screen - her eyes almost popped out of her head and her jaw dropped open. Patrick's too, as together they watched, enchanted. As if knowing it was on TV, the baby moved its head and sucked its thumb. I heard Meg catch her breath.

"Everything looks fine," Dr. Stoller said. "We'll have the results of the amnio in a week or so."

Meg and Patrick nodded wordlessly. I think if they'd had their way we would have spent the rest of their visit with me on the table! They didn't talk much on the way home, and I knew a change had taken place. They'd seen the baby now, this was for real.

"At 18 weeks I can expect to feel it kick around soon," I said. If we were starring in a *Lifetime* movie, the baby would have moved at that moment and they could have felt it and everyone would have cried tears of joy. But all was quiet the next day as I stood on the porch with Mike and Sarah and waved goodbye. Mike crossed the street to go play with Eric, and Sarah and I changed into bathing suits and went to the pool.

"Sometimes your mom makes brilliant decisions," I told her, "and having Meg and Patrick watch the amnio was just plain genius. Did you see how excited they were when they left?"

"Can I bring a toy into the pool?" She held up a plastic dinosaur.

I sighed. "If it sinks I'm not swimming to the bottom to get it, you'll have to wait for Mike."

She nodded earnestly.

"Okay." There are moments in a mother's life when she looks at her child and feels like everything makes sense, like nothing really bad can happen. Life affirms life. I grabbed Sarah and scored a big wet kiss.

"Genetically healthy!" I reported several days later.
"Hurray!"

"And guess who woke me this morning?"

Silence, then she said, "The baby?"

"Yes! That's what I wish you could experience, Meg, quickening."

"Quickening?"

"Feeling the baby move for the very first time."

"Tell me what it feels like."

"Well... know how it feels when your heart beats?"

"Yes."

"Imagine that beating down in your tummy. Soft thumping. And then, sometimes it feels like bubbles... or popcorn popping. It's really strange, I can't really compare it to anything else."

I stopped, worried that talking about it might make her sad; if I'd been her, it would have filled me with unbearably painful longing. But she asked, "Does it hurt?"

"No." I almost laughed - once again I'd forgotten that we were complete opposites. "Well, sometimes near the end it does, when they're big. Mike settled onto my bladder for what felt like a month and I was making constant runs for the bathroom."

"Sounds fun!"

"Yeah." What I wanted to say was, *It is, you have no idea how amazing it is, to create life!* "Something else happened that I wanted to tell you about. I went to a PTA meeting and one of the other mothers came over and asked when my baby was due."

"Uh huh?"

"When *my* baby was due."

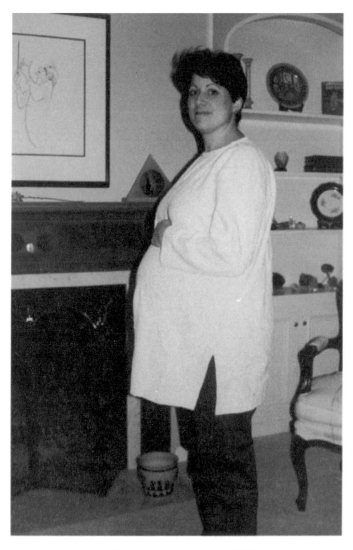

Laurie just prior to birth.

"Uh huh?"

"I didn't know how to answer."

"Why didn't you just tell her when it's due?"

"I don't know. I didn't feel honest somehow. If she had asked when are *you* due, I could have just said January."

"So what did you say"

"I said it's not my baby."

"Oh!"

"I know, she was really startled. I felt bad."

"I know that Patrick and I asked you not to tell anyone, but I mean, if it's making you uncomfortable not to explain..."

"Explaining makes me uncomfortable too."

"Why?"

"Because everyone seems so focused on the negative aspects or what might go wrong. They say, *Are you sure you're not going to change your mind after it's born?* Or, *Isn't it hard going through a pregnancy and not having a baby when you're done?* And my favorite, *How can you just give away your baby?* So I try to explain that it's not *my* baby, and the only reason it's even here is because I decided to have it so I *could* give it away. But they make me feel like I'm this horrible monster who can just give her baby away."

"Geeze, Laur! What you're doing is so brave and unselfish. It stinks that people look at you like you're doing something wrong."

"Well," I said, feeling better for having told her, "I guess I can put up with it for a few more months. How are you and Patrick doing, how's business?"

"Better, thanks. Less stress. What else there, any medical updates?"

"No, the second trimester is pretty uneventful. Baby moving and vaginal discharge."

"No details, please!" she laughed. "Talk to you later!"

I felt fat and awkward and way more tired than I'd felt during my other pregnancies. Age? Or the weird sense of detachment that had taken over, as if this pregnancy was happening to someone else? I found nothing magical in the baby's flip flops, didn't bother to alert Ken to put his hand on my tummy to share it. I told myself it was my heart gearing up to let go when the time came: *This is not your baby.*

Then I started having severe palpitations that left me struggling for breath. Dr. Stoller referred me to a cardiologist who said he was "concerned but not alarmed." I wanted to kick him - we were only talking about the organ that kept me alive! But when he hooked me up to a monitor to see if I had a mitral valve prolapse, I didn't. His diagnosis: palpitations.

In November I failed the glucose tolerance test and was at risk for gestational diabetes. I turned out not to have it, but leg cramps kept me up at night, and even caused bruising. Dr. Stoller advised me to start taking an iron supplement because I was becoming anemic.

"It just keeps getting better and better," I said to Joanne as I sampled her pumpkin muffins. But my first bite made me sad. Soon it would be Thanksgiving, and Thanksgiving always made me think of Robert.

I miss you, I said in my head a thousand times a day as if that was his new residence. *I hate that you're gone, I can't stand It! When am I going to start to heal?* I stopped attending the support group a month ago because I felt I'd reached a plateau, and lately didn't have enough energy in the evening. The only thing that helped was working on the quilt. Everyone knew that was Mom's time with her thoughts, even Sarah knew to steer clear. Through tears, I'd quilted all the hand prints. One by one, his friends had sent in their squares and I added them to the bottom.

When the phone rang, I answered reluctantly; hated to be interrupted, but Mike was in school and they had to be able to reach me.

"Hey, Laur!"

"Hey, Meg." My voice wobbled.

"Are you okay?"

I drew in a ragged breath and told her I was working on Rob's quilt. "Stitching his name across the top was bad enough, but doing the dates: when he was b-born and wh-when he d-died... he was here for s-such a sh-short t-time!" I ended on a sob.

"Yeah. Hey, want to talk later then?"

"Okay." I was glad to hang up. Tears kept spilling out, leaving my vision so blurry that I felt like Helen Keller, using my fingers to determine where the next stitch needed to be.

About half an hour later, the phone rang again.

"Hi. Laur, sorry to bother you. I don't think you should be working on the quilt right now."

Puzzled, I sat for a second, waiting for it to make sense, then said, "What?"

"It obviously upsets you. It can't be good for the baby."

"My crying doesn't affect the baby."

"You don't know that! What if the emotional stress puts you into premature labor?"

"But I'm already sad, Meg. Working on the quilt helps me release it. That's probably better than keeping it inside."

"But it makes you think about him. If you were busy doing other stuff, you wouldn't have time to brood."

"Brood?"

"You know what I mean. If you kept your mind

occupied, you wouldn't be so sad. You should do stuff that makes you happy."

Oh, you mean shut off my emotions. Good idea. I sniffled, wiped my eyes with the back of my wrist, and said, "When I was pregnant with Mike, my father left my mother to move in with her brother's ex-wife. And then Robert told me he was HIV positive. And Mike turned out fine."

"But those things were out of your control. You can control your moods. Don't sit there crying, *do* something. Read or watch TV. Just until after the baby is born."

"But working on the quilt is helping me."

"It doesn't sound like it's helping, it sounds like it's making things worse! I mean, don't take this the wrong way, but it's almost like, working on the quilt gives you an excuse to, you know, sort of wallow in self pity." When I didn't answer, she amended, "I know his death was hard on you. But you need to move forward."

"Having your baby isn't moving forward?"

"You know what I mean."

"So I should just stop thinking about him?"

"No! Of course you're going to think about him! But maybe you should just focus on the happy memories... don't sit around all day thinking about how he's gone. Think about how lucky you were to have had him in your life."

I was glad she couldn't see me shaking my head. It was like she was reading some bullshit self-help manual to avoid being sad. I wasn't even mad at her, I was just stunned that her solution was so shallow. Suppress! Don't acknowledge pain! That was Meg. "Well," I said, calmly, not defiantly, "I'm not going to stop working on the quilt. You're going to have to respect that decision."

Long silence. I pictured her scowling, helpless, miles away. Later tonight she'd blow off steam to Patrick: *I asked her flat out to stop working on the quilt and she refused!*

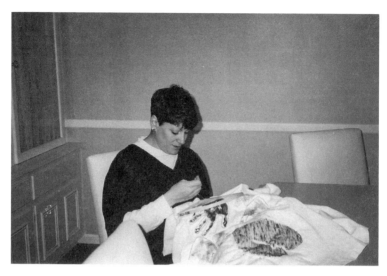

Laurie working on Rob's quilt panel.

Unwillingly, I felt sorry for her, and said, "Trust me, Meg, this won't affect the baby. If I thought it would, I'd put the quilt away. Okay?"

More silence, and then she said, "Okay," in a clipped, disapproving voice.

I ignored it; for some reason, felt better for having disobeyed her. "We'll talk in a few days, okay? Give my love to Patrick."

Joanne, John, and Eric came over for Thanksgiving, and although I tried to feel festive, I couldn't shake the gloom. Several times during dinner I escaped into the kitchen on the pretense of getting something from the refrigerator, and used the time to release tears. My throat felt so clogged that I could hardly eat. And yet I laughed, participated in the toast - *To good friends!* - and joked with Joanne about gaining weight.

Later, as we cleaned up, I said, "Isn't it amazing, when you think about human evolution, how after a big meal the women still do the dishes, and the men watch football? Do you suppose that goes back to caveman days?"

"Yes. Cavewomen picked up all the bones and half-chewed scraps of meat, and cave men sat on rocks outside and watched dinosaur fights."

"Will it ever change? Will men ever clean up while women relax?"

"Now you're just talking crazy," she said. "You need to lie down? Seriously, are you tired?"

"No, I'm okay." She was doing most of the work, transporting the tens of thousands of dishes from the table to the sink, I was just putting away condiments and covering leftovers. I didn't realize I'd let out a shaky sigh until I felt her hand on my arm.

"You made it through," she said. "You're doing great."

"Now I just have the one-year anniversary, the holidays, and his birthday."

"You'll be fine. You'll be getting ready to have a baby! If that's not a distraction, I don't know what is."

Time to Push

"I just left Dr. Stoller's office," I told Meg. "He's going to induce me on January 26th."

"I thought the due date was February 4th?"

"Well, it's been pushed up." I laughed. "Want me to tell him to push it back?"

"Ha, ha, *no*! I can't wait! I started getting the room ready, and Mom and I are buying all kinds of non-gender baby stuff. You should see her, she's like a kid!"

"It's great hearing you sound so excited," I said, feeling better than I had in a long time. "Is it finally starting to sink in that you're going to be a mom?"

"I think so! I've been so cautious and worried about getting my hopes up. Plus Patrick gets me so nervous. I think I haven't allowed myself to be happy about anything. So how are you feeling, recovering from Thanksgiving?"

"If you mean have I stepped on the scale, no. My mom and Lisa are coming for a visit this weekend, that'll be fun. They want to see the quilt, and I think we all just sort of feel the need to be together since it's almost a year since Rob died."

"Oh. Right."

A bored tone, steering clear of emotions. I should have let it go, but I didn't. "What did you feel like on the anniversary of your dad's death?"

"I just mostly didn't think about it."

"I wish I could be that way," I said, meaning, *I'm so glad I'm not!*

"Me too," she said.

"She said she just didn't think about it?" Joanne repeated when I told her.

"Yeah."

"Wow! My mom died years ago, and I always feel horrible on the anniversary of her death. I still miss her so much."

I nodded as she offered coffee; she was acting as hostess even though we were at my house, and I sat big as a barn at the kitchen table. "Maybe Meg's way is easier, being cut off. But it seems so unnatural and unhealthy to me. I think if you never grieve you can create all kinds of chaos inside and not even realize it."

"I think so too. Feeling it has to be better. Was she like that when you were kids?"

"Maybe a little, but I think after she met Patrick she sort of closed up even more. He's really private, and I think she got to be that way too." I sighed. "She was a blast when we were teenagers. Cute, and had a lot of boyfriends. But they didn't last long. I think they got scared off by her illness. Believe it or not, she was a fantastic athlete. Still is."

"Really?"

"Yeah, you'd never guess it, would you?"

"No, she looks so fragile. Like you want to take care of her."

"That's how it always was - people taking care of her. She's a little older than me, but I was always like a mother to her. I mean, that's sort of my nature anyway, to mother people, so maybe that's why we connected: I like to mother, and she likes to be mothered."

Joanne pondered it. "Probably. You don't seem to have that much else in common and now you're not just performing the ultimate act of mothering, you're giving *her* the chance to be a mother. Wonder how she'll be?"

"She'll be great, I'm sure. She's a good mom to the

dog."

"Will you watch TV with me?" asked Sarah, joining us, sleepy-eyed and dragging a ragged doll by the hair.

"Actually, it's nap time," I said.

"No!"

"Tell you what. Go get your pillow and you can lie down on the couch."

"No nap!"

"We'll put the TV on and if you can stay awake, you can watch."

"Okay!" With a little girl's determined expression, she bounded up the stairs to get her pillow.

"Works every time," I whispered to Joanne five minutes later as I shut off the TV and kissed soundly-sleeping Sarah. "My life changed the day I realized that it doesn't matter where they nap, as long as they nap."

I made it through by telling myself it was like any other day without him, it was just the anniversary of the day I lost him. Tomorrow would be the anniversary of the day after I lost him.

"You did great," Ken said as he got into bed beside me.

"Maybe I'm just too tired to be as sad as I was before. I feel like I'm a hundred years old, my legs are killing me, and I look like shit."

"You do not, you look like someone who's about to give birth."

"I look like shit," I insisted, "and I've been such a bitch. I hear myself snap at you and the kids because I'm so uncomfortable and grouchy."

"It's been hard on you, but it's almost over. And soon you'll be back to your old lovable self."

"That's the other thing," I said.

"What?"

"I know this is insane, but I'm already dreading it being over."

"Don't start."

"I know! I wish I was one of those people who lives in the moment. Remember that story about the guy being chased by a tiger and he runs and runs and gets to a cliff and the tiger is hot on his heels, and he has no choice but to leap over the cliff?"

"I'm not sure."

"So he leaps over the cliff, but he's able to grab onto a vine and doesn't fall. He decides he's going to climb down, but then he sees more tigers on the ground. Then he looks up and he sees some rats chewing the vine. He knows he's doomed."

"So what happens?" Ken asked when I paused.

"He sees strawberries growing along the wall of the cliff, and he picks one and eats it, and it's delicious."

"Well," Ken said as the message soaked in and he silently acknowledged the disparity between Zen Consciousness and my whining, "we'll visit them and they'll visit us. You'll see, it's going to be fine."

"The date of the 25th is still on, but I think you and Patrick should come down right away."

"Why? What's going on, are you okay?"

"I'm fine. But the weather's been so bad. In the past two weeks the airport has been closed twice because of snow.

What if you put off coming and then can't make it down? And miss seeing the baby being born?"

"You really think we should come now?"

"I know it won't be easy to organize yourselves right away, but yeah, I think you should try."

For once she took my advice, and they arrived on January 19th, along with Finn. Mike and Sarah immediately lost interest in Mommy's Wondrous Journey of Birth - *Lookit, Mommy, Finn can lie down and roll over! Lookit!*

Of course the weather turned sunny and clear without a flake in the sky. I regretted having made them come so early, and I was so exhausted that I didn't prepare a single meal. Even a trip up the stairs to get something from my bedroom required a solid fifteen minutes (or more) of inactivity afterwards. The worst part was the guilt; I knew Patrick had really scrambled to get things at work under control so they could leave early.

"Laur, Patrick and I are going to Foxwoods Casino tomorrow and give you guys some time to yourselves. I know you feel obligated to keep everyone entertained, and you're going to wear yourself out."

"I really love having you here," I said. "But if you want to go...."

"If you guys are gone for the day," Ken put in, "I'll take the kids to a movie and you can have time alone, Laur."

"Why does everyone want to abandon me? Am I so unpleasant to be around?"

"Of course not!" Meg hugged me. "We're just thinking about you. I know you don't sleep well at night and you're tired all day. Maybe if you have some quiet time you can nap. Finn will nap with you."

"Meg, I'm the one who begged you to come."

"I know but it's a lot of work for you. Don't forget, my mom is coming tomorrow."

How could she not see how unhappy I was with her decision? Nevertheless, the next morning she and Patrick left early, Ken took the kids out, and Finn and I were left alone.

"I don't know about you," I said to him, "but I'm going to take a bath." He didn't even open his eyes. I went upstairs and ran the water. Easing myself in, I stared, dismayed, at the 60% of my body that was above sea level. Instead of relaxing, I hit a low point, all alone in the house, too big for a bath, worried that Meg and Patrick were bored, and picturing them speaking in hushed voices at night:

Patrick:	(clearly annoyed) *Tell me again why the hell we came a week before the baby is due?*
Meg:	(trying to mollify him, but clearly annoyed too) *Laurie got all frantic and insisted we come. Since she's having our baby, how could I say no?*
Patrick:	*There are a million things I should be doing at work!*
Meg:	*I know, I know! Being here this soon is crazy!*

Cramps hit that evening as I sat and listened to everyone's adventures, and lasted for the next few days. I had no appetite - a sure sign I was going into labor.

On the 24th, Meg accompanied me to my appointment with Dr. Stoller, who examined me, then put prostaglandan jelly on my cervix.

"That induces labor?" Meg asked.

"With any luck at all. Otherwise when she comes in tomorrow I have to give her the Pit."

"What's that?"

"Pitocin. It's a drug that speeds up labor."

"Is it safe for the baby?"

"Perfectly safe."

"Not much fun for the person having the baby," I said, hoping the prostaglandan would do the trick.

"Why?"

I was glad to hear her ask so many questions. "Remember how cold the water was at camp, and when you jumped in, it was like all the breath was sucked out of your chest?"

"Uh huh."

"Pit is like that. No build-up, no prep, no easing into it. Just *boom!* you're in labor."

"Oh! I hope the jelly works."

"Me too."

"Either way, be here tomorrow morning at 7:00," Dr. Stoller said.

I could tell the jelly was doing nothing. Disappointed, I was edgy during dinner, and didn't eat much. I probably wasn't the most pleasant company, but still, I resented that Ken was keeping his distance; paying extra attention to the kids and drinking scotch with Patrick And Meg seemed irritable, telling me I had to eat a solid meal, and not being sympathetic when I said I couldn't. *"You have to eat,"* she kept saying, as if she knew everything about health and nutrition. I didn't like her mothering me, it felt unnatural. Trying to chalk it up to her being nervous, I found even that annoyed me. What was *she* nervous about? I was the one who'd be giving birth in the morning to standing-room-only audience! I'm sure we were all glad when the evening ended and everyone went to bed.

I didn't sleep much, and at 6:30 Ken walked Sarah and Mike to Joanne's house. Mike headed to school; he was the only one who'd be having a semi-normal day.

I entered with my entourage of four. Ken got stuck filling out forms, but I followed a nurse down the hall to a huge birthing room. As soon as I saw it, I felt better - there were plenty of chairs so everyone wouldn't be hanging over the bed, and there was even a separate area for the baby once it was born.

I changed into a johnny and the nurse took my blood pressure. A little high, but not out of range, and certainly to be expected. She asked how I was feeling, physically, and I said fine.

"Dr. Stoller will be right in."

"Okay, thanks." I no sooner got comfortable than he knocked on the door and entered.

"Ready?" he asked with a grin.

"As if I have a choice!" Even though it was illogical, I hoped the jelly had done the trick. But no such luck. So Dr. Stoller directed the nurse to prepare the syringe for Pitocin.

"I'm going to check back with you in an hour."

"Okay." Enviously, I watched him go. Knowing what was in store for me was suddenly overwhelming. For the first time I felt a twinge of *Oh shit, what was I thinking?*

It disappeared as soon as Ken, Meg, her mother, and Patrick joined me; exclaiming over the nice big room (only Ken, having gone through the births of Mike and Sarah had a basis for comparison) all the while, casually eyeing me.

"Not in labor yet," I reported.

"Let us know," Meg's mother grinned. Settling into a chair, she took out her knitting. Patrick stood nearby, on my right; Ken to my left. Meg, pacing between the two, asked how I felt.

"Fine for now... in a few minutes it might be a different story."

And it was. Labor came on hard and steady. I did my Lamaze breathing, but the pain was really bad. Meg's mom held one hand, Ken talked me through the contractions in a soothing voice, and Meg and Patrick stood by, helpless and horrified. For their sake, I tried not to yell too much, but the pain was so intense, much worse than with Mike or Sarah, that a few powerful yelps escaped. At one point I glanced over and saw them sort of clinging to each other, staring. I have always felt that labor in the movies is completely different from labor in real life.

Dr. Stoller showed up about an hour into it, checked me out, and said, "This isn't going to take very long!"

"No kidding!" I snapped between waves of pain.

"Hang in there, I'll be back soon."

"You're leaving?" Meg demanded, panicked. "She's going to have the baby!"

"She doesn't need me yet. Relax, everything is right on track."

Reluctantly, Meg nodded, and she and Patrick watched him go. Luxuriating in a pain-free moment between contractions, I almost laughed, thinking that their expressions reminded me of Scarlet O'Hara in that scene in *Gone with the Wind* when Dr. Meade, presiding over a field full of dying soldiers, tells her he's too busy performing emergency amputations to help deliver Melanie's baby. Another contraction hit me full force and I resumed my breathing - *whuh whuh whuh!*

"This isn't like the last two," Ken said.

"No," I said as the pain receded. "I don't know if I should be happy or scared."

"Why would you be scared?" Meg asked.

Another contraction, God they were hard, they were *so hard!* and after it passed, I answered, "I was in labor 36 hours with Mike, then had a C-section. Sarah was 15 hours. I have a feeling this baby is going to be born in about two!"

"What's worse, hard labor for less time, or easier

labor for a long time?"

Overcome with another contraction, I managed to shrug. Patrick, who hadn't spoken in about an hour, watched me with wide, terrified eyes. I kept telling myself that someday it would be funny and we'd laugh about it. *Whuh whuh whuh!*

It's a Girl!

Dr. Stoller returned in another hour, gowned and gloved. "How's everyone doing in here?" With a big smile, he put on a mask, then lifted the sheet covering my legs. "Let's take a look."

"I'm ready *now*," I said, trying to keep the urgency out of my voice so Meg and Patrick wouldn't be scared.

Ken, gripping my hand, confirmed, "Yeah, any time now."

I felt Dr. Stoller's examining finger inside me, then saw him deliver a brisk nod to the nurse. As the bottom of the bed dropped and my feet were hastily placed in stirrups, another nurse handed Meg and Patrick gowns and masks, which they quickly put on. A ferocious contraction made me howl.

"Are you ready for this, Meg?" came Dr. Stoller's voice from behind the sheet.

She didn't answer. Breathing hard, I glanced up at her, and the word that came to me was *incredulous*. "You better be ready," I managed to say, "because you're about to be a mom!"

I pushed once... twice... and at 11:58 A.M. on Friday, January 26, out slipped an eight pound, six ounce baby. "It's a girl!" I heard Dr. Stoller announce. He held her up and she was gorgeous - of course! Meg stared in speechless rapture, tears flowing down her face, clinging to her mother, who sobbed uncontrollably. Patrick looked shocked, enchanted, and said, "She's perfect!"

"Perfect!" I agreed. There are no words to describe the physical and emotional relief you feel when a baby is born;

and you hear it cry, and your husband kisses you and whispers, *"You did great, you're fantastic!"*

"Wait'll you see her cleaned up!" beamed one of the nurses, escorting them over to the part of the room that was set up to measure, clean, clear nose, and swaddle. In just a few moments, Meg, at last a mother, held her precious roaring bundle, while Ken and Patrick scrambled for their cameras. I sniffed back tears, realizing that I had turned a happy couple into a happy family. Meg's mother kept saying she never thought it would happen, she *never* thought she'd be a grandmother!

Meg walked over to me. "Want to hold her?"

"No, you enjoy her, I'll hold her later." I sighed, feeling sleepy and happy. "We did a good job, didn't we?"

"Yes! Laurie, thank you so much!"

"You're welcome. You don't feel weird, do you?"

She gazed at the baby, then her expression changed and she glanced at me. "Why would I feel weird?"

"I guess I feel weird. She came out of me, so my body is saying I just gave birth. But she doesn't look like me, Ken, or any other baby that has passed through my legs and entered the world. And my head is telling me I don't have a new baby."

When no one answered, I realized they couldn't understand what I was going through; in fact, not one single person in the whole hospital, maybe even in the whole state of Rhode Island, could relate. I wanted to say, *"It's not good or bad, it's just weird,"* but there was no point. Not sure I was even making sense, I suddenly couldn't keep my eyes open. Exhausted after such hard labor, all I wanted to do was sleep.

"Want to know her name?" I heard Meg ask.

Forcing my eyes open, I nodded.

"Jillian Laurie."

"Oh!" From somewhere deep came the energy to feel

honored, emotional, able to suddenly start to cry with big gulping sobs. "R-really?"

"Of course! We knew all along we'd give her your name if we got a girl." Pressing Jillian to her chest, she leaned over and kissed me.

I sniffled, tried to recover, grabbed a tissue. "Jillian Laurie! What a pretty name!"

"We said we didn't care if we got a boy or a girl," Patrick said, "but secretly I wanted a girl."

I laughed, picturing him 14 years from now, trying to understand her mood swings, her obsession with boys and hair and clothes and talking on the phone. They say that girls are harder to raise than boys. But why mention it now?

Dr. Stoller interrupted the scene, "I need some time with Laurie. Why don't you all head into the newborn waiting area for a bit?"

"Okay."

"Ken, you'll call my mother and Lisa and my dad?" I requested as they headed toward the door.

"I'll do it right now."

Meg turned back, tenderly kissed Jillian's tiny nose, then said in a baby's voice, "Bye bye! See you soon!"

Once they left, Dr. Stoller delivered the afterbirth, and stitched up a tear incurred during the delivery. The nurse cleaned me up, and I had a few minutes alone before they all came back. Ken had just enough time to deliver congratulatory messages from everyone when a couple of nurses showed up to transfer me to a room.

For supper the hospital served steak, and although it was nice, I wasn't planning to run out and proclaim Kent County as the new place for steak. Patrick disappeared and returned with shrimp and champagne and cake. We laughed, said *I can't believe this! Can you believe this?* about a thousand times, and every few minutes Meg or her mother or

Patrick would slip down the hall to the nursery to get another peek at Jillian. Meg smiled with delight when we agreed that Jillian looked just like her.

Ken, sitting on the bed, was quiet; held my hand, and watched me for signs of fatigue. At around 8:00 he caught me yawning, and said it was time to go.

Meg, who looked exhausted, stood. "Okay. Get a good night's sleep, Laur, we'll see you tomorrow!"

"See you, Laurie!" said Patrick. He escorted Meg and her mother out.

Ken lingered, kissed the back of my hand. "I'm so proud of you, you have no idea," he said.

"Thanks. I'm pretty proud too."

"You're okay alone? You feel like you can sleep?"

I laughed. "No problem!"

"Want me to stay?"

"No, I'm fine. Honest."

"Okay." He kissed me again, on the lips, a lover's kiss this time. "I'll be back first thing in the morning."

"Okay. Goodnight. I love you."

"I love you, too."

With a happy sigh, I watched him go. In no pain, I lay back, luxuriating in the peace and quiet.

The night nurse came in half an hour later. "Hi, Laurie, you okay?"

"Yes, fine. How's Jillian?"

"Doing great! Do you want to feed her?"

"No, thanks." I waited for her to say, *"What do you mean, you have to feed your baby!"* but she just said, "Okay," and I realized she knew about the circumstances. Thank God! I didn't feel like explaining. As soon as she left, the phone rang.

"Congratulations!"

"Thanks, Joanne."

"How do you feel?"

"Good! But it might be adrenaline. Probably tomorrow I'll feel like I got run over by a truck."

"Ken said you were amazing. He told the kids, they were so excited! Mike told the dog it has a sister."

"Wait'll you see her, she's so pretty."

"I bet! Hey..." she hesitated. "I was surprised to see Meg and Patrick home, too. Why didn't they stay?"

"Meg was really beat. She fell asleep in the chair."

"*You* had a baby and *Meg* fell asleep?"

"Yeah, well..."

"Listen, I don't like you being there alone. Want me to come over?"

"Joanne, you're so good to me! But no, thanks, I really don't mind. And I'm so tired."

"Okay. Call me if you change your mind, okay? No matter what time?"

"Thanks, I will. How were Mike and Sarah today, did they behave?"

"Of course! Eric and Mike built a snow fort with John, and Sarah and I did puzzles. At supper she said very matter-of-factly that she remembered you before you had the new baby. It was so funny!"

I laughed, longing to be home, so grateful that she called with news of *my* babies.

"Sleep tight," she said. "Don't forget, call me if you want."

"Thanks, Joanne. I love you."

"I love you too."

Meg called at 8:00 the next morning. "I miss Jillian! Isn't that silly? She's not even 24 hours old!"

"No, it's not silly at all! I think it's wonderful!" I nibbled at cold, uninteresting toast, anticipating the Dunkin Donuts coffee Ken promised to bring me. "How did you sleep?"

"Like a rock! You?"

"Like two rocks."

"Have you seen her yet this morning?"

"No. I asked about her and they said she's doing just fine."

"Oh good! Hey, Laurie...?"

"Yes?"

"I have sort of bad news. I mean it's not real bad, but..."

"What is it?"

"Well, Patrick and I have to leave earlier than we thought. Since we got here so early, we can't stay as long as you and I talked about."

Disappointment swamped me; I felt sick and couldn't answer.

"Please don't be mad! If we had gotten here when we first agreed, I think we could have stayed longer. But you know how it is when you're the boss... hard to take time off."

"But I told you I'd need some transition time! I thought you could hang out... so I could get to know Jillian, and watch you be a mom. I was looking forward to that so much!"

"I know, I'm so sorry, Laurie. I wish I could stay, I would if I could!"

"So, when will you go?"

"Tuesday."

"That's less than a week from now!"

"I know. Patrick and Finn are leaving on Monday; at least I'm staying one day longer."

"I thought you were going to be here for Sarah's

birthday?"

"Laurie, I know. I wanted to. But I just can't."

But you just won't. "You knew this was my biggest fear, you knew I didn't want to feel like, thanks for the baby, see ya later!"

"Laurie!"

"I just gave birth! I was hoping you could help me take care of my kids a little bit until I got back on my feet, and I could show you the ropes with Jillian."

"I'll be here for a little while. I'll help with everything, and by the time I go, you'll be back to your old strong self."

"But my mom and Lisa were going to come for Sarah's birthday and meet Jillian!"

"Have them come early," she suggested merrily; only her schedule mattered. "I'm sure they'd rather come early anyway! You can call them when you get home."

I shut my eyes, battled tears, forced my voice to sound steady. "Okay."

"It'll be so fun for them to see Jillian! I bet they're excited."

"Yeah."

"And maybe they can stay a little longer if you still need help."

"Yeah."

"So you're okay with this, really?"

I sighed; it was as if my end of the conversation hadn't even taken place. "Whatever, Meg. Not like I have a choice."

Any other friend would have heard my tone and felt like shit. Joanne would have stuck her head in an oven before hurting me. But not Meg! It was as if she'd gone to the baby store, picked one out, and then told the sales clerk that she had to hurry home and make supper.

"We'll be there around noon. You think they'll let us take Jillian home today?"

"I don't know."

"Well, I guess we'll find out!"

"I guess."

"Okay, see you in a little while!"

"Bye."

When Ken arrived, he was alarmed to see me in tears. "What's wrong?" he demanded, grabbing me and holding me tight. "Are you okay?"

"Meg called!" I wailed.

"Oh."

I pulled away and looked at his face. "She told you?"

"Yeah."

"I don't want her to go so soon!"

"Did you tell her?"

"Of course I told her! She doesn't care. She doesn't care about anyone but herself!" I wiped my eyes with a tissue, blew my nose. "She's horrible to do this, right? I mean, it's not me being hormonal?"

"No, it's shitty, what she's doing."

God love him for agreeing with me. I pushed my face against his chest and felt him kiss my head. "I'm going to call Mom and Lisa and see if they can come right away."

"Okay."

"Know what I hate the most?" I asked, still pressed against him.

"What."

"That Rob won't be able to see her."

Ken knew not to say, *I'm sure he can see her from where he is,* which wouldn't have made me feel better; he just held me tight, stroked my back, and waited while I cried it out. When my shoulders stopped shaking, he took my face in his hands and made me look at him. "You just did an incredible thing for Meg, and it sucks that this is how she thanks you. But that's who she is. Being mad at her isn't going to accomplish anything. It's not going to turn her into a different person, or make her stay longer. All it'll do is make things uncomfortable. And no one wants that. You have to focus on your achievement. Screw her. Can you get past this?"

"I don't know," I admitted. "I don't want to be mad at her, I want this to be such a happy time for us both. After all we went through!"

"Someone has to be bigger than this, and it has to be you."

"Shit. Why didn't I know she was going to act this way?"

"I guess you never had a baby for her before." He smiled; wise, loving. Made me feel better.

The doctor on the floor that morning released me at 11:00. I was hoping to see Meg and Patrick, but they hadn't arrived yet to pick up Jillian.

"Were they up and dressed when you left?" I asked Ken.

"They were up. Patrick was reading the paper and drinking coffee. Meg and her mother were still in their bathrobes. They didn't seem to be in much of a rush. After Mike got on the bus, I told them I was going to ask Joanne to come over, but they said they'd watch Sarah."

"Babysitting," I said, "to make up for having to leave early."

"I guess. You'd think they'd want to come right over."
"You'd think."

But when we got home, it was Joanne at the kitchen table, coloring with Sarah.

"Mommy" Sarah screeched, flying into my arms.

I couldn't lift her, but crouched and caught her in a

hug. "Hi, little one! I missed you!"

"I missed you, too, I made something for you!"

"Oh good, what?"

"Um...." She climbed back into her chair, half standing, looking through pages of scribbles until she found one, which she presented with a huge grin. "This!"

"I've never seen anything so beautiful in my whole life!" I said, taking it. "Look, Daddy!"

"Beautiful!" he agreed.

"On the fa-ridge?" she asked.

"Of course!" With her beside me, I secured it to the refrigerator with a fuzzy dog face magnet. "Wait'll Mike sees that!"

"I want to draw something for Mike," she said, going back to the table.

"I'll bring your stuff upstairs," Ken said. "Want me to run a bath?"

"I'll go up in a few for a shower."

"Okay."

I waited for him to leave, then motioned Joanne to join me out of Sarah's earshot. "How did Meg seem when they left?"

"Tired, but excited."

"And they didn't leave here until half an hour ago?"

"Yeah, I was surprised. I figured they'd tear out of the house as soon as the sun was up!"

"Meg doesn't do much tearing around in the morning, she has to do those chest treatments. But I'm worried that since she wasn't really that involved with the process, she might not feel emotionally vested."

"She will, Laurie. Maybe it'll take her a while, for that exact reason. But when she came over this morning to get me, she seemed really happy. Couldn't stop talking about Jillian."

"Really?"

"Yes! And if worse comes to worst, you and I will take Jillian."

"Don't even joke about it. I'm going to shower, I feel gross."

"Okay."

"Thanks a million for watching Sarah."

"You're welcome. Hey, Laur?"

"Yes?"

"Stop looking for things to worry about. Can you?"

"Can I stop?"

"Yes."

"No."

"Can you try?"

"Have you *met* me?"

She laughed. "Go shower."

Shielding my enormously sore, rock-hard, triple F breasts from the shower's spray, I washed away the hospital with lilac-scented soap. Shampooed my hair, then was too tired to stand any longer, got out, and lay down. Right away got up and put on underwear and a thick pad, since I'd be bleeding for several days. The stitches hurt now, and I was trying to gather up the energy to go downstairs for ibuprofen when I heard a car pull into the driveway.

I got up, went to the window, and saw Meg and her mother and Patrick get out. Patrick circled around the car and most of his body disappeared as he leaned in and unhooked Jillian from her car seat. A moment later he reappeared, holding her. A radiant smile lit up Meg's whole face, and peace swept through me again, replacing anger. *She's got some quirks, but don't we all? The important thing is, she loves this little girl, and will take good care of her.*

I got dressed and went downstairs to be with them.

The Letter

If I was a normal person, I would enjoy this, I thought, watching Meg and Patrick play with Jillian. They clearly adored her, and kept finding new features to exclaim over and admire: her gorgeous long lashes, her crystal blue eyes (I didn't have the heart to tell them that most babies' eyes are blue until the melanin in the iris stabilizes), her sweet pink cheeks, the delightful chubbiness of her arms.

But since I was neurotic and a master at finding reasons to be anxious, all I could think was that they were leaving soon; Patrick would pack up the car and the dog, hug and thank me, and then drive off. Then one day later I'd drop Meg and her mother and Jillian at the airport. Who knew when I'd see them again?

"Laurie, you seem so sad," Meg said suddenly.

Say you're fine, say you're just tired! "I feel the way I used to driving back to college after spending a weekend with my family. Dread."

Meg sighed. Patrick looked annoyed, and in a way I couldn't blame him. Life would be so much easier if I didn't complicate everything by being honest. On the other hand, why ask if you're not ready to hear the truth. I looked at Ken.

"It could be hormones," he said, an attempt to be helpful.

"Could be," I agreed, feeling betrayed, thinking how nice for everyone, if we could chalk it up to Laurie's raging hormones! That my mother and Lisa had been unable to accommodate Meg's change of plans only added to my resentment. "I guess I just really loved us doing this, and I hate to see it end."

"It's not ending! It's just beginning!" Meg said. "We've only had her one day and already you're thinking about what's going to happen down the road."

"Just try to be happy," Patrick said.

"I'm happy," I said, resisting a sulk. *Try to be happy,* what stupid advice, like something you'd read in one of those self-help books that tells you to just get over stuff. "Of course I'm happy."

"Hey," Ken said, touching my shoulder, "What about the little, you know..."

"Oh, right!" I stood, slowly and painfully - the stitches hurt like hell. "I have something for Jillian." There was silence as I headed for the stairs. Were they exchanging glances? I hated when I said something and people exchanged glances.

In the top drawer of my dresser was a child's locket that I'd bought for Jillian a few months earlier. I took it out and held it up and pictured her wearing it. When she was old enough to understand the circumstances surrounding her birth, she'd tell friends, *It was a gift from a woman who loved my mother so much that she would do anything for her.* Ugh, so sentimental! Maybe Ken was right, maybe it was hormones. If Rob was alive I would have called him and told him. What would he have said? Probably, *Focus on what you did, focus on Jillian.* He had a way of keeping it simple. I put the locket back into the box. Maybe the less you personalize something, the easier it is to dismiss it. *Don't let her get to you,* he'd say.

When I went back down, they were talking about pizza for supper, and having Joanne and John and Eric over.

"You feel like having company?" Ken asked me.

"They're not company, they're family," I said; lowering myself onto the couch next to Meg, I handed her the box.

She opened it. "Oh, Laurie, I love it!"

"It has a ruby in it. My birth stone."

"Thank you! Did you put a picture in it?"

"No, that's your job."

"I'm sure she'll want a picture of her daddy in it," Patrick said. He reached over and took Jillian from Meg, kissing her nose. In his arms she was so tiny, so delicate. So pale.

"I have to be honest," I said, "yellow isn't a good color for her."

"What?" Meg stared at me, then at Jillian. "What do you mean?"

"It makes her skin look yellow. Let's try a different color. We want her to look nice for when Joanne comes over tonight."

Without questioning my judgment, Meg took Jillian from Patrick, and she and I went into the guest room. But even in pink, something wasn't right.

"You know what, Meg? I think she's jaundiced!"

"Is that bad?"

"It's not good. What time is the visiting nurse coming?"

"Two."

"Let's see what she says."

"Jaundice," confirmed the nurse immediately. She gently pressed her finger against Jillian's forehead, and it left a yellowish mark. "Definitely."

"Will she be okay?"

"You should bring her back to the hospital and have the doctor look at her."

"Thank God this happened before you left!" I said.

With the four of them gone, the house was quiet. Finn, used to the comings and goings of her humans, took up residence on the couch at my feet.

"You okay?" Ken asked.

"Actually, I'm in agony where I got stitches."

"Want something for the pain?"

"I took three ibuprofen, they haven't helped at all."

"Are you worried?"

"A little." I sighed. "I don't have the energy for another emergency, but I can't stand this."

"I'm going to take you in. Call Joanne and see if she can watch Sarah."

"Okay." I reached for the phone. "I'm glad Joanne doesn't charge by the hour!"

"Congratulations," Dr. Stoller said. "You ripped a stitch."

"What now?"

"I'll give you something for the pain." His voice turned stern. "Laurie, this happened because you're doing too much."

"I'm not, really."

"Well a stitch doesn't just rip out. You have two little kids and a house full of company. You think that just because you don't have to take care of the baby, you can go back to your normal routine. But you have to take it easy. Okay?"

"Okay."

"We had to leave her there," Meg reported when they returned a few hours later. "She's going to spend the night under a light."

"But she'll be okay?"

"Yeah, we'll go get her tomorrow."

"It's weird that they wouldn't let you stay overnight with her," Ken said.

"We could have, they offered to set up cots. But us being there wouldn't really serve a purpose." Meg yawned. "And I wouldn't have slept well. Don't forget, I've spent a lot of time in the hospital."

I just stood and stared, unable to decide if I was impressed by how sensible she was, or if I was horrified by her lack of emotion. For the first time, doubt prodded me.

"Are we still on for pizza?" Patrick asked. "We're buying."

The next morning Meg called the hospital to check on Jillian. When she hung up, she said, "We can go get her!"

I took pleasure in the relief and joy on her face. Maybe I'd been unfair - after all, I was the one who hadn't even wanted to hold my babies after they were born, and they'd come out of my body! Who was I to judge Meg's emotional attachment to her child? I couldn't know how she was feeling any more than she could know how I was feeling. We were at opposite sides of the circumstances. I vowed from that moment to give her the benefit of the doubt.

Patrick and Finn left early the next morning. He said he hated leaving his "girls," and Meg said she'd be home soon, she couldn't wait. It was easy to see that she would have given anything to be leaving with him. In a way, it was gratifying, because it meant she cared about me enough to stay; on the other hand, it hurt, because if she really cared about me, she would have wanted to stay.

I felt draggy and sad all day, but somehow I managed to resist the urge to talk about anything serious. After supper Meg said she was exhausted and asked if I would give Jillian her last bottle and put her to bed.

"She's pretty, isn't she?" I asked Ken as we lay in bed

with her between us, waiting for her to be tired enough to sleep.

"Not as pretty as Sarah, but yeah. Know what the best part is?"

"What?"

"When she wakes at 4:00 and you and I can just roll over and go back to sleep!"

"That *is* exciting," I laughed. Then my mood turned. "I'm not looking forward to tomorrow."

"I know, but it'll be okay. We'll visit them over the summer. I mean, you've sometimes gone years without seeing each other. We can plan to see them at least once a year. Could you be satisfied with that?"

"Yes, I think I could do that. Or maybe twice the first year. I can't wait to see Jillian in her own little room."

Our eyes went to her, nearly asleep, tiny bubbles forming in the corner of her mouth. Precious in the way only babies can be. Looking at her made me think everything was going to be fine, just like Ken said.

"Thanks for giving Jillian her bath," Meg said, coming into my room.

"You're welcome. Did you get all your packing done?"

"Finally. How come it took so long? I've only been here a couple of weeks!"

"Well now you have baby stuff." I held Jillian up. "How does she look?"

"Like the most beautiful baby girl *ever*!" Gently taking Jillian into her arms, she was so careful, so loving. "You've been such a huge help, Laur. I have no idea how I'm ever going to get her and me out of the house on time."

"You feel that way now, but once you get home she'll get settled and everything will be easier."

"What do you mean settled?"

"Babies take a few weeks to find a routine. You'll know when it happens - she'll start sleeping longer and be happier when she wakes up. You'll see."

"I hope you're right."

"I know I am. You're going to be a great mother."

After dropping them at the airport, I stopped at the store to pick up stuff for Sarah's birthday, specifically french fries, party hats, and a tiara. My breasts, the size of watermelons and just as hard, ached with every step, bouncing no matter how slowly I walked. It was snowing and I worried about the flight; wished I had made Meg promise to call as soon as she got home.

The first thing that hit me when I walked into the house was the baby smell. Carrying the groceries into the kitchen, I spotted two nipple covers that had been left behind. I put the food away and called Joanne to see if she'd mind bringing Sarah back. "I feel like such a slug, but the idea of crossing the street to get her is like climbing Everest."

"Don't be silly, I'll come right over."

"Thanks."

She arrived a few minutes later with Sarah and my mail, which included a baby magazine and an offer for free diapers. I put them with the nipple covers, intending to send them to Meg along with the photos I'd be picking up the next day. My mother and Lisa would be arriving the following evening, and I had a ton of laundry to do before then. Battling weariness, I filled Joanne in on the latest.

"Meg isn't the most demonstrative person," Joanne

declared, "but I could see how grateful she was. And she loves that little girl. So does Patrick."

"I know. I'm not worried. I just feel let down somehow." I made myself laugh. "But if I wasn't complaining about something, I'd have nothing to do."

"Come on," she said, "you've had an emotional year, and now you need to get back into the swing of not being pregnant with someone else's baby. It might not be easy. Don't think you're going to be back on top right away."

"Permission to sulk," I said, grateful.

Sarah appeared, and rested her head on my knee. "Let's watch cartoons."

"Okay," I said; I could tell from her expression and voice that she would be asleep within minutes and wouldn't notice if I slipped back into the kitchen. "What's on?"

"Don't know."

We went into the den. I flipped around, found something she liked, and sat next to her on the couch. "Want to watch lying down?"

She nodded, lay down, and just like that, *out*. I smiled, wondering when Meg would learn how to read Jillian's moods.

When I went back into the kitchen, Joanne was pouring herself a second cup of coffee. "Did you get balloons?"

"Pink and yellow. She's going to love the bracelet you bought her, I can't wait for her to see it."

"I remember when I was a little girl my Auntie Rose gave me a bracelet and I felt so grown up." Joanne filled my cup again too, and we both sat.

"Just think," I said, "a year from now, Jillian will be one year old!"

Joanne, who was raising her cup to her lips, laughed.

"What?" I said.

"I thought you said you were going to try to stay in the moment!"

"Ohhh... right." I sighed, and sipped. If life had taught me anything lately, it was that. But why was it so hard to do?

The next morning the phone rang very early. "Hi, birthday girl's mom!" said a hearty voice. "How are you?"

I squinted and rubbed my eyes. "Patrick?"

"Yes! I wanted to be the first to wish Sarah a happy birthday!"

"You are. She's not even up yet. I'm not even up yet."

"Oh, sorry! I have a million things to do today and knew I wouldn't be able to call later."

"No, I'm glad you did, I'll tell her." I sat up. "So how's Jillian?"

"She's great, Meg's great. Everyone is doing just great. It's amazing to have a baby around! To hear that little squeaky cry first thing in the morning, and see all the little tiny clothes in the hamper."

I smiled; as if he was the first person to experience it! "She slept okay?"

"Like a pebble."

"Good. Hey, Patrick, I'm glad you called. I wanted to talk to you about coming up in April for Meg's shower. I could surprise her. Joanne said she'd drive up with me if the flight was too expensive."

He hesitated for what felt like a long time, then said, "I don't think that's a good idea."

"Why not?"

"Because it's Meg's shower and it should be about her and the baby. It's her time to be the center of attention. If you're there, it'll be about you, the surrogate. That's not fair to her."

That sudden sick feeling again; hurt and disbelief. At

that moment Sarah came into the room, and without a word, I handed her the phone and said, "It's Patrick."

She took it excitedly. "Hi, Patrick, is Finn there?"

I didn't listen in on the conversation at all, just got out of bed, went into the bathroom and washed my face and brushed my hair. When I came out, she'd hung up and was back in her room. I could hear her talking to her dolls. I took a deep breath and wondered how I'd make it through the day.

"Is it me?" I asked Joanne an hour later. "Seriously, is it me?"

"No! That's horrible, what he said! I can't get over it!"

Her outrage was my green light to cry, and cry I did - big, loud sobs that shook my shoulders. I felt her hand on my back, rubbing, rubbing. "How could he not know how hurtful that was?"

"I don't know," she said. "I have no idea."

She came with me to pick up the photos, and we blew up balloons while Sarah napped, and hid them in the broom closet. My mother and Lisa arrived with cheerfully-wrapped gifts that Sarah went ahead and opened without waiting for Ken to come home. She sort of helped bake the cake, and for dinner we had lasagne and salad, and, of course, french fries. Pretending everything was fine started to wear on me, and as soon as the kids went into the den to watch television, I told everyone what Patrick said.

There was shocked silence. Tears flooded my mother's eyes. Ken simply stood and walked out of the room, too angry to speak. Lisa sat shaking her head. John, who'd obviously been told ahead by Joanne, said he couldn't believe the way Patrick was treating me, just couldn't believe it.

We looked up as Ken returned.

"Okay," he said, "just tell me you're kidding. That Patrick didn't say that."

"I wish I could."

He sat down and blew out a sigh; took my hand and said, "I just *hate* this for you."

"If you hadn't been the surrogate you would be invited," Lisa pointed out. "How screwed up is that?"

"You'd think she'd be so proud to show off the friend who did such a wonderful thing for her!" my mother added.

"I just think I'm a source of embarrassment to them," I said. "Like a reminder of their failure or something."

"That's so unfair!" John said.

"I wonder if Meg knows that Patrick told me not to come? If she knows, I'll feel so awkward calling to see how she and Jillian are doing. Obviously I want to know, I don't think that's asking a lot!"

"Of course not! You have every right to know!" my mother said.

"This is just so wrong. After what you did, it's just so wrong!" Ken shook his head.

I stood and started gathering dishes. I was glad everyone agreed with me. But what good did it do?

February 17, 1996
Hi, Guys,

I just got off the phone with Meg. I decided to sit down and write to you because after several attempts on my part to initiate a discussion over the phone, I find myself resorting to the place that I find most comfortable: writing.

A lot of stuff is going through my head. I know this is natural, given what we've just gone through. I thought I might share some of it with you. I'm trying very hard to adjust to our new roles. It seems when I talk to Meg on the phone, things between us are strained. I don't know if it's me or us or what. Having a new baby can be overwhelming, giving birth to a baby is overwhelming, and the way we did it is monumentally overwhelming! I'm sure all these factors contribute to a feeling that I would call "awkward." So right now I'm trying to figure out where I fit in.

For over twenty years, Meg and I have had a very close long-distance friendship where we spoke sometimes only once a month. Then, for a two-year period, we talked with more frequency and had an amazing bond - we shared the goal of having a baby. Now I discover that I don't know what the status of "us" is anymore. I'm sure it will take a little while for us to find that out.

I don't know if you feel this uneasiness, Meg. Maybe it's just me, maybe it's hormones. All I know is that our relationship must change due to the nature of what has transpired, and I have to find a way to deal with that, in addition to everything else I'm dealing with.

When I spoke to Patrick about coming to the baby shower, he didn't seem to realize that I wanted to surprise you, Meg, and be part of your day. I don't even know if he told you I wanted to come. But when he said not to, I was so hurt, even though I know he wasn't trying to be mean. I guess I didn't like being called "the surrogate" the way he said it. I don't think of myself as a surrogate, I think of myself as your friend. I carried your baby out of love for you both. When Patrick said he didn't want me to come to the shower, I felt like I'd outlived my usefulness. Like you thought it was time for me to step out of the picture and leave you two (three) to go on with your lives without me. Patrick, I know you were just trying to protect Meg. I appreciate that, and your honesty, but it doesn't make me hurt any less.

I wanted to share Meg's shower. I wanted to be part of watching her play that role that she has so longed to play: mom. I hope you know me well enough to know that I would never have come intending to steal the show. I would not have been comfortable with people making a fuss over what I did, and I don't think that would have lasted more than a few minutes. Meg and Jillian most certainly would have been the centers of attention. When we threw Meg a little shower here before Jillian was born, she was the star, not me. It would have been that way at her shower there, too, I'm sure of it.

To see Jillian in her new home, to see Meg being a mother - I would have loved that. I tried to understand why you had to leave here when you did, but it had been my fear all along, that we'd have the baby and then you'd leave before I was ready to let you go. I even told you that, Meg, how much it meant to me to have you stay here for a while after she was born. I guess I sort of felt like a hostess left to clean up after a party.

I really want to feel good about what we did, not "Okay, what do I do with myself now?"

I hope you can understand how I'm feeling. If you don't want me at the shower, I understand. I have no choice but to understand, because the very worst thing that could happen would be to end this journey on an unhappy note. None of us wants that. It's just that it's easy for you to move on - you have your little angel and you're busy with her. But I can't move on until certain things happen, one of which would be for me to see Jillian happy and safe in her crib.

This letter was very difficult to write. I hope you can appreciate my honesty, as I appreciated Patrick's. I think one of the reasons I had such a hard time with it is because I am so used to putting other people's feelings before mine, and I was tempted to just swallow Patrick's words and not voice how hurt I was. That's what I usually do, I'm really good at that. But this is too important. I have given you two years of my life, and a beautiful little girl that I am so proud of. I don't want resentment to ruin that. They say that honesty is the best policy. I think it is.

I love you guys,

Laur

Send a Quilt Out to the World and it will Envelope You in Love

The ringing phone interrupted my progress on the final touches on Rob's quilt. Reluctantly, I answered, "Hello?"

"It's Meg."

"Oh, hi! How are you? How's Jillian?"

"Laurie! How could you write such a letter?"

She sounds mad, I thought, *but she can't be!* "I just thought it was the best way to tell you how I'm feeling. I tried to bring it up a few times, but I didn't do a good job. But now that you have the letter, we can talk about it."

"I don't *want* to talk about it! I don't think I ever want to talk to you again!"

I tried to figure out what I'd written that was so upsetting to her. "What do you mean?"

"That you could accuse me of being an unfit mother!"

"*What?*"

"You said you needed to come up here and see Jillian safe in her crib! Why do you think she wouldn't be safe?"

"Meg! Are you serious? I just said it like, just a figure of speech! That I wanted to see her happy and safe!"

"Well it didn't sound like that!"

"Come on! Do you think I would carry a baby for you if I didn't think you were going to be a good mother?"

"You know what pisses me off the most? That you dumped this on me! Why couldn't you talk to Joanne or Ken or your mother?"

"I did, Meg! But I needed to talk to *you* about it, you and Patrick. I was really really hurt by what he said. I wanted to talk about it so that I could understand why he said it, then

I could move past it."

"Well I can't move past this letter! You know, Laurie, you're not the only one whose feelings have been hurt over the past year! And I never said a word to you, I dealt with it *on my own!*"

I was stunned. "But our rule was that we were supposed to talk about everything! We promised to be honest with each other!"

"I kept a lot of stuff inside out of respect for you, and I don't know why you couldn't have done the same for me!"

"What stuff?"

"It doesn't matter now."

"Of course it does! What did I say that hurt you, that you had to keep inside?"

"Okay, since you *have* to know... when you were in labor and Dr. Stoller asked if I was ready. Before I could even answer, you said, *You better be ready!* Can you imagine how I felt? Being so insecure and nervous? I would have loved a little reassurance! Not some stupid sarcastic wisecrack!"

I couldn't even speak. *That* bothered her? *That* was what she'd had to deal with on her own? "You're kidding me, right?"

"No, Laurie, I'm not like you, *I* don't have to joke about everything, *I* can be serious when I need to be."

"Meg! I was in *labor!* Women in labor say all kinds of things! Plus, I was having *your* baby! I'm supposed to make *you* feel better while your baby's head is splitting the skin of my vagina and I'm in such agony that I can't even think straight?"

"God, there you go, being so dramatic! I have to hang up. Don't call me back, I don't want to talk to you."

I heard *click* then silence. For a second I just sat and stared at the phone. "No way!" I shouted. "No way are *you* mad at *me!*" Heart thudding, I dialed Joanne's number.

"Hi," she said. "Let me guess - you just got off the phone with Meg."

"How'd you know?"

"Because she called here first. I tried to calm her down, but she wasn't even making sense! I told her not to call you."

"I can't get over this! I can't figure her out!"

"I know. It's insane. You should be relaxing and feeling like a hero, not dealing with this bullshit. What are you going to do?"

"I don't know, Joanne. I can't think of anything right now. Maybe I'll come up with something. But right now I'm too upset."

"I don't blame you."

"She told you she was mad about what I said during labor?"

"Yeah. I told her that no one is responsible for what they say during labor! She just doesn't know, she's never been pregnant."

Suddenly I was tired, too tired to even hold up the phone. "Joanne, I'm going to lie down for a while. Call you later?"

"Of course! Anytime!"

"Thanks." I wished Meg could hear what a real friend sounded like.

Ken, who had seen the letter before I sent it, was dumbfounded. "There was nothing bad in there!" he fumed. "And even if there was, even if it was the nastiest letter ever written... *you gave her a baby.*"

My parents were furious. So was Lisa, so was everyone I told. Everyone wanted details. I heard myself going over it again and again, and finally got sick of the whole thing. So I stopped talking about it. But I didn't stop thinking about it. Every time the phone rang, I was sure it was her; I was sure she was going to apologize for being so bitchy. *"That's okay,"* I was going to say; *"You have a lot on your mind."* She'd say, *"Having a baby is so much more work than I thought it would be! And you had two! How did you do it?"*

But as days gathered into weeks and the phone didn't ring, I tried to let go of the hurt and focus on my own children. It was time to make up for the months of dropping them off at Joanne's for each health crisis. Sarah and I played with her dolls while Mike was at school, and in the afternoons after he got home the three of us did whatever they wanted - colored, watched cartoons, or played games. I insisted that Joanne leave Eric with me as much as she wanted so that she and John could have some alone time.

I finished Rob's quilt, and on March 10th we participated in an AIDS quilt dedication ceremony held in the JCC in my home town. Rob's panel hung behind the podium, and I stood and addressed the audience of over a hundred:

Dear Robert,

Night after night I lovingly and painstakingly embroidered your quilt panel. Every stitch reminded me of you, of us, of how desperately I miss you. I know you were watching every stitch. I felt your hand guiding me. I heard your voice chastise me for missing a stitch. I heard you laughing. I cried your tears.

Twenty-five people were involved in putting your panel together, twenty-five people who wanted to honor you. And I felt your hand in them all. You were in charge of us all, you orchestrated the process. This is as it should be, for you wouldn't have had it any other way.

I think if you were still on this physical plane, this quilt would have enveloped you in love and warmed you on your journey to the next dimension. It would have eased your pain as you listened to us remember those things about you that we love. But even though you're not on this plane, I know you're here with us today, watching from another place. I feel your presence.

Each square that one of your friends tenderly created for your panel represents something special that you gave them. There isn't a panel big enough to celebrate all that you have meant to us. We had to struggle to express our emotions on a small 12 x 12 area. Above that, our hands, intertwined and reaching up to a broken heart. Our hearts are broken, but we know the hardest thing for you to do was leave us, and we felt your heart break too.

As we finish this quilt and dedicate it to your memory, we are reminded of the enormous impact you had - and continue to have - on so many lives, and the lessons of love you left behind. I see it in the eyes of my children as they remember you. I hear it in their voices when they say, "I miss my Robert." But I tell them to close their eyes and picture you. Sometimes the picture makes them sad, but usually it is your incredible smile that comes to them, and I see joy on their faces. Thank you for that smile.

A few days later I had my six-week follow up exam with Dr. Stoller. He greeted me with a hug, then asked if I'd brought pictures of Jillian.

"I forgot them, I'm sorry," I said.

"Oh." He was obviously disappointed. "Well! How are you feeling?"

"Great. Like my old self."

"How's Meg doing, is she all settled in?"

"She's great. A pro."

"Tell her I was asking for her. Tell her I knew she'd be fine!"

"I will. I'll tell her next time I talk to her."

"Will you be going up there for Christmas?"

I pretended to be occupied with my wedding ring, then my watch. "Yeah, we'll probably stay through New Years."

"Bet you're looking forward to that!"

"Yes." I nodded. "I am."

I hated lying to him, this wonderful doctor-turned-friend who had gone through so much with me. But how could I tell him that Meg and I weren't even speaking?

"Why didn't you just tell him what happened?" Joanne asked. It was one of those suddenly, freakishly warm New England not-quite-spring days, and we were sitting outside drinking coffee while Sarah looked for butterflies.

"I'm not sure. I went in not knowing how I would handle it, I was just going to play it by ear. And then I just heard myself lie. But while I was driving home I realized I lied because I feel like what happened is a reflection of me. I failed."

"How can you think that?"

"Maybe I don't think I failed, maybe I think other people will think that. Everyone who doubted me in the beginning, everyone who didn't think it could work... I guess in a way they turned out to be right. I dedicated myself to this, to giving Meg a baby, and in the end, I have nothing to show for it but heartache."

"Meg," echoed Sarah, half listening.

I lowered my voice. "I never thought I was noble or brave to do this, the way some people said I was. But I surely don't think I deserve to feel like shit about it."

"Well," Joanne sipped coffee, "in all my thoughts about how this would work out, It never once occurred to me that it would end with her being mad at you. So that just goes to show you - it doesn't pay to make assumptions. People never act the way you think they're going to."

"I can't believe I didn't see this coming. She's so touchy and aloof. I should have known that she..."

"Laurie," Joanne's voice turned stern. "The first thing you have to do is stop blaming yourself. You did an amazing thing. Nothing can take that away. She's got problems, not you."

"I like being outside," Sarah announced. She came over and leaned against me. "I like being outside with you, Mommy."

"I like being outside with you too, Sarah," I said, pressing her head against my chest so she couldn't see the tears in my eyes.

"There's your proof," Joanne said. "The next time you worry that you did something wrong, look at your kids."

Joanne and John and Eric came over for Mike's eighth birthday on March 30th, and I was just about to serve when the phone rang. Ken answered, and I could tell from his cool tone that it was Patrick. He glanced at me: *Want to talk to*

him? I shook my head. "Thanks for calling," he said, "I'll put Mike on."

Mike, feeling important, reached for the phone. He obviously knew nothing about the tense dynamics, and chatted about the cake Sarah and I made. I had no interest in discussing the call, and was glad when Ken said not a word, just took the phone from Mike and hung it up when he was done.

On Monday there was a note from Meg in the mailbox. With heart pounding, I tore it open, not sure what to expect. To my surprise it was a birth announcement. Nothing else.

When Ken came home, I handed it to him. He looked at it and handed it back.

"Am I wrong to expect that she could have taken an extra second to write me a personal note, or include a picture or something?"

"You're not wrong," he said. "It's just that she doesn't do things the way you and I would." He sighed. "Maybe sending it was her way of saying she wants to be back in touch with you. I mean, she could have *not* sent it."

"True." I put it back in the envelope. "It just feels like I'm on the same list as her hairdresser and her mother's bridge partners. But without me there wouldn't be a birth to announce!"

A few days later the phone rang as I was coming in from the supermarket. I set my bags on the counter and nodded when Sarah asked if she could have a glass of juice. Picking up the phone, I said, "Hello?"

"Laurie?"

My heart felt like it was being squeezed, but I managed to sound calm. "Hi, Meg."

"How are you?"

"Fine." I poured Sarah her juice and sent her into the

den with it.

"What's going on down there? Patrick called Mike on his birthday, and you didn't talk to him."

"He didn't ask to talk to me."

"He didn't think he had to! He assumed you'd want to say hello and see how we are."

"I was busy with dinner."

There was silence, then she said, "Are you okay? You sound upset."

I stared at the phone. "I sound upset?"

"Yes. What's the matter?"

"You said you didn't want to talk to me and you dropped out of my life for a month! So now you call out of the blue and want to know why I'm upset?"

"Oh, Laurie, can't we put that conversation behind us? Let it go. I have."

"Because you're not the one who was hurt! You said some horrible things to me! And now you want to just act like it didn't happen!"

"I didn't mean to hurt you."

"You did so, Meg! You had every intention of hurting me! You know there was nothing in that letter to justify the way you treated me!"

"Well I'm sorry you feel that way."

"Wanna know how else I feel, Meg? Like you and Patrick came here and borrowed a cup of sugar and then went home. Like that's all it meant to you."

"Laurie! We don't... we're not... it was just that stupid letter!"

"That letter was *not* stupid! It was me opening up to you and telling you how I honestly felt! What was stupid was my hope that you'd actually *hear* what I was saying. But no, you turned it into something it wasn't, just so you could be defensive and outraged."

"I don't want to talk about the letter."

"You know what, Meg? I don't either. I want to talk about what *happened*, what prompted me to write the letter. And until you're ready to talk about *that*, we have nothing to say to each other."

"Fine!"

Someone Else's Birthday

"We need a vacation more than any other family in the country," Ken said that evening after I told him about the conversation. "Let's take the kids to Disney World. They need to have some fun, and it'll be good for us to get away from everything."

"That sounds great! I'll make reservations tomorrow." I wasn't really looking forward to it; stress was devouring my energy. But he was right, the kids deserved it.

It turned out to be a very good idea. Being away from my surroundings and away from the phone was like being released from prison. Not that my mind shut down altogether! But I was able to relax, and as Ken and the kids and I strolled in the warm Florida sun, we joked about missing the grimy piles of snow back home.

One afternoon as we ate dinner with Minnie and Mickey, Mike picked up a blank postcard that was lying on the table. "Can I send this to Jillian?"

"Of course." As I fished through my purse for a pen, I wondered how Meg would feel when she saw it. Would that upset her too? I pictured coming home to an angry message on my answering machine: *"How could you have Mike send me a card? Why didn't you send one too? You didn't even sign his!"* I sighed, so tired of worrying about her reaction to everything. It was just a post card, for crying out loud.

"Welcome home!" Joanne said when I called her. "Did you have fun?"

"We really did!"

"Did the kids swim?"

"Mike did. Sarah stayed pretty close to shore. We have a bag full of broken, dirty shells they *had* to have, plus two dead crabs."

"I'm so glad you went, you sound good. How were the kids during the flight?"

"So good! Mike's new favorite thing in the whole wide world is flying. Sarah slept practically the whole time. Does it get any better than that?"

"No!" she laughed, then her voice turned serious. "I really don't know if I should tell you this... Meg called me."

"She did?"

"Twice."

"What did she say?"

"Believe it or not, she still doesn't know why you're... what was the word she used... *distant.*"

"She has no idea, does she."

"No. She kept saying, *'But what's wrong? Do you know what's wrong?'* I tried to tell her, Laur... I said you were hurt about the shower, and when you tried to explain that she bit your head off. It's so weird, she wasn't hearing me at all."

"What did she say?"

"Oh..." long hesitation. I could picture her shuffling through the conversation, censoring anything she knew would hurt me. When she finally said, "Not too much," I realized that probably most of it had been bad. "She's just weird."

"Was she mad?"

"No, she was hurt. I have a feeling she'll call you."

And she did, two days later. "Listen," she said. I could

hear the phone momentarily traveling through dead air, and then soft cooing.

"Is that Jillian?" I asked.

"Yeah. She makes that sound when she's happy. I wanted you to hear it."

Tears filled my eyes and my voice went wobbly. "Thanks, Meg. I'm so glad you shared it with me."

"Can we talk about what happened? When Mike's card came and I realized you'd gone to Disney World and not even told me, I knew we had to fix things."

"I don't know. I want to, Meg. But it's so much more complicated now than when I tried to fix things a few months ago."

"Because of that stupid letter! But let's try to forget it. I want things to go back to the way they were."

"They can't, Meg. And even if they could, I wouldn't want to go back."

"Do me a favor and don't get all dramatic."

"I'm not! But I want to move forward. And the only way to do that is for you and Patrick to find a place for me in your family. I want more from our friendship."

"Laurie, honest to God, I'm doing the best I can, but I'm not like you, I don't go running to the phone every time I break a fingernail! You should know after 20 years of being friends that we're just different people."

"Very different," I agreed bitterly. "When I look back over our 20 years I feel like it's mostly been me trying to keep in touch."

"That's not true, I've called you!"

"Yeah, when you wanted help or advice. When a guy ditched you and you didn't know why. When your sister was acting like an ass and you needed me to agree with you. When you were trying to figure out if you should work for your dad or do something else. When Patrick came home obliterated that night and you were in hysterics. I've been taking care of you since you were sixteen! I'm not saying that I regret any of it, or that I wouldn't do it again; I would. But when I needed *your* help, you turned your back on me." When she didn't respond, I pushed forward. "What we've been through completely changed the way I view our friendship, and I don't think it's changed your view at all. I had your baby, and now we're back to where we started. That was life altering for me, Meg!"

"It was life altering for me, too! Obviously!"

"Maybe that's true, but you have a funny way of showing it or sharing it with me! You went out of your way to push me aside!"

"I didn't push you aside... you were just too much in my face about stuff."

"Calling to see how the baby is, you call that in your face?"

"No, it's how you always *analyze* everything! Always have to tell me about every single precious feeling you have: You're hurt. You're depressed about Rob. You're feeling lonely. You need an adjustment period. It gets exhausting! No wonder I don't want to call you! It always turns into a lecture!"

"It does not!" Her sarcastic tone made me feel sick. "I mean, I wouldn't have to ask you to call if you would just do the right thing and call! It's like asking you to donate a kidney!"

She sighed, a hostile, impatient sound. "I'm really aggravated right now, I don't want to talk any more. Here's what I think: I think we need to cool off before we try to work this out."

"Well here's what *I* think: We're not going to work this out until you come to grips with the fact that you didn't physically have Jillian. I did."

"Oh God, here we go again! Like I don't know that? Like you don't throw it in my face every five seconds?"

"I'm not throwing it in your face! I'm just saying that I don't think either of us knew the impact it would have on you. We both thought, *Oh good, we'll have a baby*, but we never considered how it would affect you emotionally. I think you're feeling guilty or inadequate or something, and you're taking it out on me."

"Maybe *you* feel inadequate," she said.

"What? Why would *I* feel inadequate?"

"Maybe your life isn't fulfilling enough, so you had to do something like this."

She stopped, and I had a feeling she was just trying to hurt my feelings. And the fact that she wanted to hurt my feelings *did* hurt my feelings. "Hey, Meg? I love that you shared Jillian with me today. And I love that you called and want to fix things. I know that was a big step for you, and it means a lot to me. Let's just see how it goes from here, okay? Can we?"

In a subdued voice she said, "Okay."

On Mother's Day I received a beautiful floral arrangement and the note: *Hope you have a nice Mother's Day, as we will. Love, Meg, Patrick, and Jillian.* Thrilled, I called her, but had to leave a message.

Inexplicably, a week passed. I drove myself crazy trying to figure out why she wouldn't return my call. She couldn't be mad about the message I left... could she? Over and over I reviewed it in my head, recalling to the best of my ability that it went something like, *Hey, you guys, thanks so much for the flowers! I love them! They're gorgeous! Call me... bye!* Should I have sent her flowers too?

"I don't know if I'll be able to visit you every day at the psychiatric ward," Ken said, "but I'll come by on the weekends, and I'll bring the kids."

"It's just weird, her not calling me back. Isn't it?"

"Meg is weird. Why does it keep surprising you?"

Finally I called her again. "Meg, I'm so glad I caught you. Thanks so much for the flowers!"

"You're welcome."

"Are you okay?"

"No, Laurie, we're not. Ray and Sally's son was killed the day after Mother's Day."

"Oh my God! What happened?"

"He was removing a tree from someone's property and the tree fell on him and crushed him. He was only 24!"

"Oh Meg, I'm so sorry! That's horrible! Poor Ray and Sally!"

"I know. They're devastated."

Reaching for a pen and a pad of paper I said, "Can I have their address?"

"Why?"

"To send them a card! Is that okay?"

"Oh! Okay. Sure."

As I wrote it down, I thought about Ken's comment, about her always surprising me. And for the first time it occurred to me that maybe I kept surprising her, too.

Dear Laurie and Ken,

How kind of you to write a note of sympathy and encouragement to us. I did not realize you had lost a brother. It is a very sad

occasion when a soul mate passes. I also believe that there is somewhere around us possibly another dimension, where all the life force and energy gather for whatever purpose unknown to us. His physical presence is not here with us, but we can feel his presence both here and at the cottage. We were (and still are) a very close family. We thought we were the happiest people on earth. So many exciting things were happening. What a wonderful thing that you brought Jillian into the world to start the process all over again!
Sincerely, Sally and Ray

I was moved by her simple, beautiful, sensitive note; at the same time, annoyed: these were Meg's best friends, and she hadn't told them about Rob passing away while I was trying to conceive their baby. What a huge, shameful secret I was!

A month slipped by. Spring turned to summer, and I kept busy working in the yard and opening the pool. A dozen times I picked up the phone to call Meg; a dozen times I put it down. Incredible that she didn't know how much I wanted to hear from her, wanted to know how Jillian was.

Each day my mailbox was stuffed not only with baby-related coupons and ads, but medical bills. I kept forwarding them to Meg, but within a week I'd get another, meaning they weren't being taken care of.

"We'll just have to pay them," Ken said grimly.

"No. I refuse."

"Now is not the time for outrage, Laur. Our name is

on the bills, so it's our credit that's on the line."

I sighed hard and deep. "This just keeps getting worse. If the situation was reversed and my girlfriend had a baby for me, I would go *out of my way* to do whatever it took to make things easy for her. I would never ever put her through this! I mean, not paying the bills? Come on!"

"I know, this really shocks me. But what can we do? If they're not going to pay, they're not going to pay. So we have to."

On my birthday I got a card from Meg. Inside was a picture of four-month old Jillian. *Hope you have a great day!* said the card. I waited a few weeks, then responded with a note too.

August 27, 1996
Hi,

How has your summer been? I can't believe it's almost over! The kids go back to school on September 4. Haven't heard from you in a while. I can only assume the princess is keeping you very busy!

I have gotten two collection notifications, one from the hospital and one from my pediatrician. If there is a money problem, could you please let me know?!?

How is everyone? How are Ray and Sally? How was the humidity this summer? Ours wasn't bad at all. I hope it was not too difficult for you there.

Well, off for now. Hope to hear from you soon!
Laur

A week later, I heard back.

September 3, 1996
Dear Laurie,

As you can see, I have enclosed the money orders. I have had them for a while, but was sick and couldn't get them to you. I'm starting to feel a little better. I still don't have much of a voice, but it's coming back slowly.

The summer has gone by quickly and we have had a busy one. Patrick's father had a heart attack in June. He's okay, but still having chest pains. He's undergoing some testing, but with the major cutbacks occurring in our healthcare system and it being summer, there is no official diagnosis or plan for him of yet.

My mom is recovering from pneumonia. She had a virus for over a month and then it went into that. It has taken a lot out of her.

Jillian is doing just great and is cute as a button! She is now sitting up on her own and babbling away. She is eating meats and veggies and so far loves everything.

It sounds like Mike and Sarah had a good summer and a busy one. Did they take their usual swimming lessons? Jillian has spent some time floating around in the pool and just loves it. She and Finn have a terrific *relationship. Jillian smiles whenever she sees her and giggles when she gets kisses. Finn is also her "face cloth" after lunch. Finn is definitely happy that Jillian is eating real food now!*

Patrick is fine. He's building for a number of clients as well as building his spec houses. He's had a very busy summer, and the fall looks to be as well.

The weather here has been good too.

Anyway, I'm going to close now, as I can hear Jillian waking from her nap. Hello to Ken, the kids, and Joanne from us.
Love, Meg

Two people writing like mere acquaintances. Two people writing because speaking was too uncomfortable. Two people who shared one of life's most amazing miracles, now reduced to talking about the weather. At least she finally made good on the bills.

December 11, 1996
Dear Laurie, Ken, Mike, and Sarah,

Hope everyone is well. There's certainly lots of colds and flu going around - it's the season again. Jillian had lots of fun on Halloween. She dressed up for her music class, as did the other babies. They all looked so cute. At night we took her out to a few of our neighbors' houses. She is crawling everywhere now, and fast, and pulling herself up on whatever she can. She's busy-busy! Take care, and Happy Hanukkah.

Love, Meg, Patrick, Jillian and Finn

She'd enclosed two pictures of Jillian: one at seven and a half months, and one dressed in the Halloween costume I had given her. I ached, thinking about all the growing up I was missing.

Mike looked up with a bright smile as I walked into the den. "Is Jillian coming for the holidays mom?"

Dismayed, I sat next to him on the couch. "I'm not sure."

"Let's call and ask. This'll be her first Hanukkah - she should spend it with us."

I hated how my heart fell right into the fantasy: the three of them here - with Finn, of course - enjoying sumptuous meals and warm evenings chatting while a fire crackled; Mike asking earnestly, *Can I hold the baby if I'm wicked wicked careful?* and Meg, smiling: *As long as you're wicked wicked careful!* The most manipulative part of me thought about having him call and ask... his eager little voice, how could she say No? But unhappy logic invaded. Forcing her to come wouldn't make me feel better. I wanted it to come from her. "I'll ask her when she calls me," I said.

"I like Jee-yun," Sarah declared, joining us on the couch.

I put an arm around both, kissed one head then the other, and thought, *Could this conversation be any more of a bummer?*

"Know who else likes Jee-yun?"

"Who, honey?"

"Uncle Rob. When he visits, he says it."

That familiar stab of pain, with an intensity that hadn't diminished, could still take my breath away. "What does he say?"

She shrugged. "That he likes her."

I hoped for more details, but she was done, and slid off the couch. Mike turned the TV on with the remote, and I went into the kitchen to get supper ready. In other words, life went on.

A few days later Mike asked again if Jillian would be spending her first Hanukkah with us.

"I don't think so, honey," I said. "Meg and Patrick are very busy."

"Doin' what?"

"Well the holidays are a busy time for grownups."

"Kay." He nodded, disappointed. It was the last time he ever brought it up.

Nineteen-ninety-seven dawned bitter cold, but sunny and dry. For several days I'd been debating whether or not to get Jillian a birthday gift.

"It's crazy," I told Joanne. "If any of my other friends had a one-year old, I wouldn't hesitate for even a second. But for one that I actually gave birth to, I'm not sure. What if I send something that Meg doesn't approve of, or gets mad at?"

"If you send something that makes her mad, you can be sure she'll let you know," Joanne said wryly. "What are you thinking?"

"A book."

"Well, Laurie, you can't go wrong with a book."

"You think I should do it?"

"Yes. And a little note. You're so good at those."

"Okay." I sipped my coffee, stared out the window, felt uneasy.

At the bookstore Mike went to the kids' section, and Sarah and I browsed the baby books. In a few minutes I found just what I wanted - *On The Day You Were Born*, by Debra Fraiser. I brought it home and on the inside cover wrote: *Then I kissed your tiny forehead and whispered, "Our journey is at an end. Your journey, like the deep blue ocean, is a never-ending sea of hope. Love, Laurie."*

I sent it off on the 15th of January to make absolutely sure it would be there before her birthday on the 26th.

The Last Letter

Sometimes you do something, and later you wonder if it was a good idea. Other times you do something and a peace settles over you, and you know it was the right thing to do, even though it may not be what someone else would do, and it may not even be what you would have done ten years ago, or five, or even one.

When Jillian's birthday came and went without a call from Meg, my mind started to buzz, really buzz. For some reason, it just didn't occur to me that she wouldn't acknowledge the day. I was so uncharacteristically positive that she'd call that I hadn't even worse case scenario'd what would happen if she didn't. I hung around the house all day waiting for the phone to ring and her to say, *"Oh Laurie! A whole year! Isn't it amazing?"*

I waited almost a week, going through the motions of getting Mike to school each day, and putting supper on the table each night. Sarah and I played, shopped for groceries, and did little projects together around the house. But once the kids were in bed, I'd corner Ken either on the couch, in the kitchen, once even in the bathroom. "Can you believe this?" I must have said fifty times. "Can you believe she didn't even call me?"

Finally he exploded. "I can't keep having this conversation, Laurie! Nothing ever changes! You're driving me crazy, dragging around here like you're dead! You never laugh, you never talk about anything else! Get over it! And if you can't get over it, talk to Joanne or your mother or Lisa! But not to me! *I can't take it anymore!"*

Shattered, I watched him storm out of the room. In the den, the television came on. Loud. My heart was pounding so hard that I wondered if I was going to pass out. Standing there I realized two things: that I wasn't mad at him for shouting at me; and that he was right, I had to get over it.

January 31, 1997
Dear Meg,

I am writing to tell you that I have decided I can no longer continue our friendship. This has been a difficult decision for me, but one that I feel is best.

On Jillian's birthday, the situation I found myself in came sharply into focus. I deluded myself into thinking you would call to acknowledge that one year ago I was in labor with your child. But you didn't call, did you? You couldn't even find it in yourself to thank me for the gift I sent her. I don't ask for much, Meg, but I never thought I would be reduced to begging you for simple, human decency. To treat me as if I didn't exist on Jillian's birthday caused a hurt that can never be reconciled.

Ending our friendship won't take away the hurt, but it will take away my constant expectations that one day you will wake up, look into Jillian's beautiful eyes, and realize how truly blessed you were to have known me.

I feel nothing but sadness for you, and for Jillian, knowing that you have taken my love and been so careless with it. Your actions show me that either consciously or unconsciously you have most likely made the decision that Jillian will never know the miracle of her existence. I can only hope you will share it with her, so she can see a living example of friendship. What a lesson in love that would be for her!

If you can, for a moment, I would like you to think about what this all means. It doesn't just affect us, Meg, but our families. Jillian will never have the benefit of knowing my kids, and I had hoped they would be forever friends, the way I thought you and I were. You have known my mother and my sister for a long time, and I felt part of your life, too. I love your mother like I love my own. I wept when your father died. Ending the friendship ends all of those bonds.

This makes me so sad, but I feel I have no choice.

I leave you with one final thought: no matter what you do with this letter, no matter what you tell Jillian or don't tell her, I carried two of your children and gave birth to the one you gaze upon each night. I did that out of love for you during the most difficult time of my life. My blood runs through her veins, and no matter how you may try to twist this letter or the events that have transpired, you can't take that away from me. That's mine forever.

*I wish you and your family good
health. I hope you can find peace with all of
this.*
Laurie

Naturally the one time I hoped she wouldn't call, she did.

"Laurie! I can't *believe* you would send me another one of your horrible letters!"

"This is the first time you've called me since August!"

"And because of that you have to end the friendship?"

"I have to end it because I can't keep setting myself up for hurt over and over. And you know what? I have a feeling this is what you wanted anyway."

"Oh that's great, Laurie, that's just great! Blame me! You write this incredibly mean letter, then say I'm the one who wants to end the friendship! All because I don't call you very often? Come on! You know I was never much of a phone person."

"I had a baby for you! You can't pick up the phone every couple of weeks? God, Meg! I was so clear about this, right from the start, that once we had the baby I would need to be involved. Not in taking care of her or telling you what to do. But I wanted you to include me in her first tooth, her first words, the first time she sat by herself or stood or spoke."

"I try to involve you, I do the best I can! But she keeps me so busy..."

"I have *two* kids, and I can still find time for friends! I really wanted Jillian to know me. But I wanted you to want that too, and you don't. You just keep pushing me away."

"You're doing this, not me! If you hadn't written that

first letter, we wouldn't even be having this conversation!"

"Meg! I told you, I wrote that letter *for a reason*! I felt like once you got your baby, you deliberately started snubbing me."

"I did not!"

"You didn't even acknowledge the gift I sent! Did you get it?"

"Yes, and to be honest, I thought it was weird. Who sends a book to a one-year old? She can't read!"

"It was for you to read to her!"

"But she's not going to understand it!"

"Did you even look at it?"

"I read what you wrote inside the cover and didn't need to read anymore."

"Why?"

"It was just... *weird.*"

I sighed, tried to stay calm. "Okay, you thought it was weird. But Meg, how could you not at least call me on the day that marked the one-year anniversary of the most amazing thing we've done together? I thought about you all day. Did I even cross your mind once?"

"You didn't give me a chance to say this before, but we all had a stomach bug that day."

"What about the day after or the day after? Is it too much to ask for a simple phone call?"

"You know what, Laurie? Nothing I could have done would have made you happy! If I called you every day, you still would have found something to be mad about!"

"Me mad? I'm never mad, I'm the one jumping through hoops to keep you from being mad!"

"Well I don't see you jumping through any hoops right now! Sounds like you're *trying* to upset me! And you're succeeding!"

"I'm not trying to upset you, I'm trying to tell you

how I feel."

"That's all you do, is tell me how you feel!"

"Well if you ever listened, I wouldn't have to keep telling you over and over."

"Okay," she said in a mock patient voice, "tell me how you feel."

Like hanging up! I thought, but kept my voice steady. "I feel like you violated my trust."

"Now you sound like a psychologist. *Violated your trust.* Come on!"

"You did! When we agreed to try this, the *one thing* I asked you to do, you didn't do!"

"What was the *one thing?*"

I stared at the phone. Did she honestly not know? "I asked you not to make me feel like I outlived my usefulness once I handed you your baby."

"Seems to me you asked for a lot of things! You asked me to always be honest if something bothered me. You asked me to come mourn with you after you lost the first baby. And you asked me to come to Rhode Island four days early!"

"I asked," I said, "because I had to. Anyone else, I wouldn't have had to."

"Why can't you just accept that we're different people, who do everything differently?"

"Because it's more than that."

"No, it's not! It's *that!* You tell everyone every single thing you think and feel. I don't."

"I know you don't want to hear it, but I honestly think you're alienating me because you haven't dealt with the fact that I had the baby not *you - don't interrupt me!*" I said when she started to sputter. "You resent me, and it would be easier if I wasn't in your life, because I'm a reminder that you couldn't..."

"I refuse to listen to this! Everything was fine until

that letter."

"Everything was fine for you! Don't you get it, Meg? It's easy for you to say *Let's go back to the way we were.* But that's impossible for me. And it kills me that you want to go back to one letter or phone call every six months. I hate that that's enough for you."

"Maybe I'd call more often if you didn't chew me out every time."

"No," I said, "You wouldn't. Face it: you don't want to have anything to do with me. But you don't have the guts to admit it. You'd rather act like everything is fine, except that occasionally you have to call crazy Laurie or send her a picture. But what you'd love is to never see me again. That way you could go on with your life as if I never existed. And no one would need to know the shameful truth."

"Stop! Stop talking and stop analyzing me and stop pretending you know everything!" She took a deep breath. "This conversation is going nowhere. Let's both take some time to cool down. I need to get over the anger I feel about these letters. Don't call me for a while."

I started to cry. "Meg," I said quietly, "don't you understand? I'm not going to call you ever again."

"You're doing this!" She started to cry too. "This is your decision, not mine!"

"I just can't keep letting this tear me apart. I hope that one day you understand why I wrote the letters. I'll always love you, but I…"

"And I hope that one day you realize I'm not the horrible bitch you think I am!"

"I never said you were a horrible bitch!" But she had already hung up. So that was that. My stomach twisting in knots, I sat in silence, mourning; then gave way to tears. Of release and relief? I hoped so, but it didn't feel like it.

When Ken got home that night, he noticed I was quiet

during dinner. Promptly assuming the roll of Interested in Every Detail Parent, he kept the kids talking and laughing and eating. As soon as they finished, he got them settled in the den, came into the kitchen, and found me crying as I did the dishes.

"You ended it with Meg," he said.

Without looking at him, I nodded. *Please don't say you told me so, please don't give me advice.* So upset I was shaking.

He put his arms around me and I felt his breath on my neck. "You did the right thing," was all he said.

A year or so later, Joanne and John and Eric moved back to California. When Ken's job sent him to Massachusetts in 1998, I was only too happy to leave the house that had hosted so many unhappy memories. Once Sarah started school, I went back to work full time as a paralegal. Life settled into a more comfortable groove. We all made new friends; a normal family, undistinguishable from our neighbors. I was proud to talk about Rob, but told very few people about having been a surrogate.

The years didn't diminish my bitterness, and I would still lay awake some nights, trying to come up with one single thing she could say that would make it okay. *I'm so sorry, Laurie!* wouldn't be good enough. Ditto, *Please forgive me, I was wrong.* Even my favorite, *You were right about everything. I started seeing a therapist and she made me see why I treated you the way I did, and it was exactly what you said: I felt inadequate* didn't soften me. When I realized that nothing she could say or do would ever change anything, I thought I finally had the closure I needed. I tried to feel good about it; like everyone said, I did an amazing thing, I made a dream come true and brought a beautiful life into the world.

Of course I never stopping thinking about Jillian. Was she playful and girlish the way Meg had been? Or closed off and secretive like her dad?

In January of 2001, the phone rang, and when I answered it, I was shocked to hear Patrick say, "I have bad news. Meg passed away."

I couldn't speak. My legs gave way and I dropped onto a chair.

"Laurie, are you there?"

"Yes! I... oh my God! What happened?"

"She was really sick over the winter and I kept having to take her to the hospital. She was staying in for longer and longer stretches, and then she just... didn't come home again."

"When is the funeral? I'll come up!"

"She died in July."

"*July?*" When he didn't answer, I said, "How's her mom? I have to write to her, is she still at the same address? How are you, how is Jillian?"

"Jillian is pretty young, I don't think she understands what happened. Meg's mom is okay." He took a deep breath. "I almost didn't call you."

"Why?"

"Because Meg never recovered from what you did to her. She wasn't strong to begin with, and after you ended the friendship, she sort of went downhill."

Shock, disbelief, and then the most ferocious rage I had ever known flooded me. "There is no way you're blaming me for her death!"

"I am. I hold you responsible, in part, for what happened to her."

His voice so cruel, so cold, not even human. As if from far away I watched my hand gently put the phone back onto the base. It took several minutes for my mind to be able to process the news. I pictured Meg lying in the hospital, her final days; scared, struggling for breath, too upset to call... and knew right away it didn't add up. I wasn't so important to her that she died because I withdrew my affection. That was Patrick being his usual manipulative self, trying to make me feel bad. I let out a deep breath. Rather than do the right thing and call me to let me know she was so sick, he did nothing. And now, six months later, he did the worst thing he could think of. To punish me. For what? I doubted I'd ever know.

Afterword

In every parent's life are the milestones of their children: first step, first word, first grade. Braces, driver's license, first date, first broken heart. In the fall of 2006, Mike started college. A few months later, Jillian turned eleven.

Of course grownups have milestones too. Sometimes they are tied to their children and sometimes they are just the bumps that just seem to pop up along the road. Like everything in life, you either jump over them, go around them or fall flat on your face on top of them. My personal favorite milestone is the first day I realized that I was no longer mad at Meg or Patrick. People act in ways that mystify us, and we can either freak out, or move on. Freaking out has always been my preferred approach, but realistically, how many years can a freak out last? As I mature, I'm able to look back and see how I could have been more patient with Meg; more understanding of our differences. Maybe if I hadn't ended the friendship, I could have gotten used to her need for distance, could have accepted that she wasn't trying to hurt me, she was just doing what she had to do, to make her world work. If I hadn't ended the friendship, I could have had the bedside scene I mourned for a long time, the one where she says, *"We did an amazing, thing, huh Laurie?" I take her hand and stroke the thin, pale skin. "We sure did." She sighs. "I was never able to tell you how much it meant to me, all that you did." I assure her that I know how much she appreciated it. Jillian is evidence of a happy, loving home. "You were a great mother," I tell her. Her eyes shut because she is very tired and doesn't have much time left, but she smiles. "I was, wasn't I?"*

Last year a good friend of mine lost her brother to cancer. Sarah promptly asked for her address, and wrote, *I know how you feel, and I know that it's hard sometimes, but the most important thing is to try to be the best person you can be. That's what your brother would have wanted you to be. I know, because it's what my uncle Rob would have wanted me to be.*

That he continues to guide her after all these years is proof that his spirit lives. Which means that Meg's spirit lives too. I picture them in that Other Dimension: my friend Susan, who visited to prepare me for what was to come... my brother Rob, who makes his presence known daily in subtle ways to help me get through... and Meg, who gave me the opportunity to be the best person I could be.

Sarah and Michael visiting Rob's quilt at its first local
display at Montclair State University in New Jersey.

Acknowledgements

I am deeply grateful to so many people for their help throughout the writing of this book. To my editor, confidant, friend and the ultimate obi wan Robin Stratton, who kept me going, even after I was so discouraged by others.

To my family and friends, too many to mention by name: you all supported me throughout my physical journey and then again during my spiritual one.

To my husband Ken, who gives me the freedom to be me.

To Michael and Sarah: my inspirations and my reasons for being. Everything would be simply meaningless without you.

Biography

Laurie Miller was born and raised in Essex County, New Jersey. She lived in Rhode Island for five years, where the events of My Body, Their Baby occurred.

Laurie now lives in Southeastern Massachusetts with her husband and teenage daughter who spends most of her non-academic life on a soccer field. Laurie's son attends college in Pennsylvania and he occasionally graces the family with his presence, words of wisdom and a truckload of laundry.

To contact Laurie please visit www.mybodytheirbaby.com.